GROW A DAMN

TYLER THRASHER

GROW A DAMN

By Tyler Thrasher // @tylerthrasherart // tylerthrasher.com

Edited by Jeremy Luther
Design & Layout by Jeremy Luther // @jeremyluther // jeremyluther.com

Printed in Canada

ISBN: 978-0-578-68838-1

Dedicated
to the ranters, lovers and warriors
who grow a damn.

And to Jerry Addington,
who I'm fairly certain took a wrong turn on his way to druidic nirvana, but is making the best out of his short detour by filling the world with his love for the planet and the plants that cover it.

GROW *a* DAMN

A Plant Journal

to help growers approach their plants through

PASSIONATE, SCIENTIFIC OBSERVATION & NOTE-TAKING

If I can't help you keep your plants alive, at least you'll have enough info to write their obituary.

BY
TYLER THRASHER

Contents

Foreword

Is there anything Tyler Thrasher can't do? A talented chemist, artist, and writer, Thrasher proves doing what you love is the ultimate success.

The ***Grow a Damn*** plant journal is the latest of his brilliant projects and a great way to keep track of your favorite plants. The journal is easy to use, and accessible to botanists and hobbyists alike.

In it, he shows us the importance of curiosity as the means to grow better plants. Full of growing tips, the Grow a Damn plant journal is a great way to cut through some of the chaos of growing plants by writing down your ideas and observations about your favorite plants.

Enid Offolter

Introduction

When I'm not screaming into the void of my greenhouse, I am doing my absolute best to grow the healthiest happiest plants I can. Through my shortcomings and trials- I realized that I was in dire need of a journal. One that would help organize all of the info I was quickly gathering about the plants I loved and grew. After realizing nothing would serve my needs- I decided to make that journal myself and while I'm at it, print a few thousand extra…so I hope someone else likes it because I don't have THAT many plants.

In some form or another, I've spent my entire life around plants and growing them. My childhood was literally nurtured in greenhouses and nurseries, helping my father tend to a wholesale amount of landscape flowers and plants and in some cases I lived in these greenhouses. Plants nurtured me through some of the darker chapters of my life and the shelter and comfort I found in them yielded a lifelong relationship and passion. I literally talked my wife into buying the house we have now because it had a greenhouse in the backyard.

For the last several years I've grown hundreds of succulents and cacti—primarily species that aren't readily available and require an intensive and specific amount of care and observation. My need for a journal erupted after I realized there were over 70 varieties of conophytum in my greenhouse and I learned some were summer flowering rather than the fall flowering species I was so used to. I almost lost it, people! I mean what am I supposed to do when a Lithops Optica "ruby" mutation enters dormancy 3 months later than my other lithops and is trying to flower when the greenhouse exceeds 100F?!

If you didn't understand a word of what I just said, this book is for you; it will help you learn the terms and disciplines needed to become a proud plant parent. If all of what I just said rings clear like the halcyon call of your maker, then this book is for you! It can help you organize your thoughts and help recognize and undo any of the bad habits we all pick up as we learn. Every page, category and section in this journal was very thought out. If I had a need or an observation it would have space in this book. I want this journal to serve your needs as well and feel personal. My hope is that these pages balance a fine line between a journal that makes room for your thoughts and personality while offering organizational tips from a human who desperately needs them and is wildly obsessive over his plants.

I hope this journal grows good for ya. <3

Fertilizer

All things die. Those dead things feed other living things and so on and so on. Not all matter becomes water, but instead it will decay into other minerals and atoms. What I'm getting at is, feed your plants!

Of course, feed your plants responsibly. Fertilizing and feeding your plants will most likely require a bit of research and note-taking, as one mindless feeding can lead to a leggy overgrown plant or even spell death for them. Some tropicals are heavy feeders while succulents need a minimal amount of nutrients. Carnivorous plants get everything they need above the soil and so on.

When deciding on a fertilizing regimen, do your research, try and speak to experienced growers who might gladly share the routine they've utilized for 3 decades, or they may tell you to piss off. Life's an adventure!

This section will touch briefly on micro and macro nutrients and those little numbers you'll find on any fertilizer package.

Actually lets start with those numbers. When shopping for a fertilizer, you'll usually spot a series of numbers (hopefully easy to find) on the packing "X-X-X." These numbers aren't so much plant parent porn (or maybe they are?) but are the fertilizer's grade, and refer to the percentage of available nutrients in the mixture.

The first number references the available amount of Nitrogen (N), the second number the available amount of Phosphate (P), and the third the available amount of Potassium (K).

As an example, a fertilizer labeled "6-6-6" (yikes) will have 6% Nitrogen, 6% Phosphate, 6% Potassium, and 100% Demons. Probably. I dunno. SCIENCE!

Fertilizers are widely available in several common variations of the nutrients mentioned above. A good starting point is to pick an equal parts fertilizer like a 10-10-10 and dilute as needed for your purposes. A go-to for a lot of succulents is to pick a fertilizer like one mentioned above and dilute it in water to 10%, especially for those hardy plants known to grow in quartz fields or granite bowls.

Plants have different needs that we should observe and respect, possibly looking back to their habitats and what millions of years of evolution lead to. Do your damn homework before you break out your floppy hat and favorite Insta-filter, PlantMomKaren69!

Nutrients take the form of salts beneath the soil. When plants consume those salts, they're taken up in the form of ions, which are good because of reasons.

Plants require macronutrients and micronutrients to remain vigorous and healthy. Some examples are:

Macronutrients: nitrogen (N), phosphorus (P), potassium (K), calcium (Ca), sulfur (S), magnesium (Mg), carbon (C), oxygen (O), hydrogen (H)

Micronutrients: iron (Fe), boron (B), chlorine (Cl), manganese (Mn), zinc (Zn), copper (Cu), molybdenum (Mo), nickel (Ni)

Pests

When dealing with nature, don't forget that nature deals with *us*. Remember this as you slip into the maddening void where fungus gnats swarm like an apocalyptic army, mealy bugs move in the dead of night like fuzzy cloaked rogues, and if you have thrips: you're f****d. Sorry, I meant *fucked.*

Here I will outline the best solutions and approaches to what *we* call a pest, and what nature calls her beautiful children simply looking for a life-sustaining meal.

Mealy Bugs

If you're finding spots of white cottony material on the underside of your leaves- you may have mealy bugs. If you're finding small fuzzy white insects on the tips of new growth- you may have mealy bugs. Another sign of these dreaded creatures are ants. Ants farm mealy bugs like horrid hell-born cattle for the sap they secrete. If you're finding caravans of ants going to and from your pots, isolate the source, check for mealy bugs and destroy them.

Solution: I use a mixture of water, isopropyl alcohol and dish soap. The Dish soap removes the waxy coating surrounding the insects and their eggs so the alcohol can penetrate and do the job. I usually mix 1 part alcohol to 5 parts water with a healthy dollop of dish soap (the kind that can remove oil from ducks.) I start by spraying individual colonies or simply taking a Q tip to directly to them, when I want a more personal touch. If the infestation is too great, and you feel the plant is worth salvaging AND small enough, you can unpot it and dunk it in the mixture mentioned above several times. Repeat whichever process you choose until you've won a victory for the ages, and songs will be sung of this day.

Spider mites

When you begin to notice light webbing, a light speckled appearance on your leaves and tiny red dots swarming your plant- you got spider mites. These are best dealt with immediately as they tend to spread quite rapidly.

Solution: Spider mites thrive in a dry environment, so the first step should be constant misting of your leaves (if it doesn't harm the plant) and watering directly from above as well. Neem oil should be a well-stocked weapon in your arsenal and a constant application when it comes to spider mites. Buying a vial of predatory mites will also aid in your fight. However, sometimes the best approach is simply tossing the plant in the bin if the infestation is too great. Spider mites tend to pick favorites, and this is something I've directly observed in my greenhouse as well as others. Several different species and genera can surround the spider mites, but often times they'll stick to what they like.

Aphids

Often found on outdoor plants where growth and food are plentiful. If you're finding small black or yellow jewel like specks swarming newer growth on your plants, you have aphids. Better yet, ants also farm these similar to mealy bugs. Aphids can be quite resilient to most methods of extermination, and I often find them on plants I intend to consume so the more hardcore approaches will also serve to harm me later down the line.

Solution: One of my preferred methods is to turn the hose on jet and blast most of them off. I then take my mealy bug mixture mentioned above and apply a very generous and heart felt amount. In a healthy garden or environment, aphids don't thrive for long as they have numerous predators, and once word spreads its over fairly quick for the aphids. However, this is where the ants pay their dues. The very ants farming the aphids also defend them. There are numerous methods for maintaining and controlling ant populations. I recommend utilizing whichever one makes you feel the least guilty.

Fungus Gnats

If you notice small insects taking flight every time you water your plants or shift the soil, you may have fungus gnats. If you notice small specks occasionally fly past your face or up your nose throughout a house full of plants- you may have fungus gnats.

Solution: Fungus gnats require unwavering patience, diligence and several different approaches all applied simultaneously as you're targeting the adults, larvae and eggs. I start by allowing the soil and pot to dry out more than usual. I then water with a mixture (4 parts water 1 part hydrogen peroxide). This will kill any and all larvae and eggs on contact. You'll then notice the adults swarm from the pot for safety. Little do they know, you had a barrier of sticky fly paper awaiting them, ever so gently draped across the surface of the soil. This will catch any and all adults and consequently cut down on the number of fungus gnats reproducing. You should repeat this process as often as possible as any eggs or larvae you miss will only carry on to repopulate the infestation.

Thrips

A hell-ridden army to undo all other armies. There are thousands of species of thrips and chances are you may have to wage war against one of them. If you notice small speckled discoloration on the leaves of your plants, if you see small white insects flee in unison into the crevices of your succulents, or watch as they scatter up and down the stem to avoid you— you most likely have thrips.

Pest control for thrips is best utilized when you first see the insect rather than the small puncture marks they leave. Thrip damage isn't evident until the plant grows and expands, which is not an accurate indicator of the current thrip situation. Respond to the insects, not the visual damage.

Solution: A healthy and constant application of neem oil and other contact oils like horticultural oils. Make a diligent effort to locate the insects and apply the spray directly to them. A single female can lay 80 eggs at once, which will hatch in only a few days during warm weather- so constant vigilance is key.

If it comes to it, systemics can also be utilized but ONLY as a last ditch effort. Systemics can be toxic to humans, animals and especially pollinators. I would only recommend using systemics in a greenhouse or potted plant scenario to prevent the chemicals from leeching into thc soil and effecting other plants. As another safety precaution, consider applying a systemic only after the plants flowering period or cycle. Systemics are pulled into the plant and this can include the flower and its pollen.

A FEW OVERALL SUGGESTIONS:

Inspect *every* plant before you buy it. Often times a plant can appear lush and happy when sharing a bench with dozens of similar plants until you lift it and spot mealy bugs having a shaded picnic on the underside of the leaves. Nurseries don't necessarily have the time to check all of their plants for pests let alone treat thousands daily so any pest patrol will have to be done on your watch.

If you purchase a plant online, ALWAYS quarantine it. This sounds like an extra step between seeing the plant and bringing it into your collection, but its a necessary step. Quarantining can be a separate room away from your collection and other plants, or a plastic tote with a lid that you lift periodically to check for pests. The maximum quarantine time I suggest as well as other growers I respect is no more than a month. Any eggs or pests that hitched a ride will usually rear their ugly faces within a month. There are some exceptions however, such as pests that won't hatch until warm weather resumes.

When you spot a pest, check all adjacent plants and pots. Remove those plants from the rest of the collection immediately, send them to your quarantine area and begin executing the attack. Do not reintegrate that plant until at least two weeks after you've decided the pests have been eradicated.

And finally, wash all gardening tools, pots, and reusable labels in dish soap, bleach, and rubbing alcohol when dealing with pests. This is especially important for any pots you wish to keep after losing or removing the plant. Eggs and larvae can cling to the edge of the pot and will definitely await their next meal.

Soil Additives

It's all about the dirt, baby. When it comes to your plants, soil should be at the forefront of your mind. The most luxurious and exotic plants will crumble into their own mortality with a neglectful soil mixture, and you'll find succulents and cacti giving you a spiny middle finger while they laugh and violently rot at your attempts to yet again add builder's sand to their soil. Different roots have different needs, and *a lot* of consideration should be utilized when navigating the perfect soil for your plants. This could be as simple as purchasing a pre-made mixture and adding a little somethin'-somethin' or building your soil from scratch.

On this page you will find some of the more common and accessible amendments and components used within the hobby and things I've found to serve my own personal needs. I can not stress this enough- without the right soil and foundation- all of your efforts will eventually lead to the same result (DEATH). If there's something we can learn from our plants its that our roots are the unseen workers that stabilize everything up top. If you take care of your roots, the rest will follow.

Akadama A highly porous clay mined in Japan. Akadama is well known in the world of bonsai but has useful applications in other plant circles. The porous nature of akadama means it soaks up excess water and nutrients to be released when the soil dries. Akadama also has a dark appearance when moist which can be a useful indicator for watering purposes.

Bark/ Mulch These components help with water retention and break down slowly while releasing nutrients at the same time.

Charcoal (Horticultural) Charcoal can raise the pH of your soil, increase drainage, and aid against compaction.

Clay Helps with water retention and releases moisture as the soil dries. Clays can be rich in organic material from years of break-down and decomposition and are an excellent source for beneficial minerals. Clays can concrete and drastically lower aeration however and should always be mixed with attentiveness.

Coarse Sand Primarily used to add drainage to your soil mix. Coarse/ sharp sand can also help enhance the structure of your soil mixture and provide excellent support for root systems.

Coco coir Excellent for moisture retention. Coco coir is incredibly light and adds

aeration to your soil mix and dries out while still keeping its integrity. It also helps retain nutrients for plants.

Compost Adds an incredible source for organic matter and nutrients. Composts break down slower than a lot of synthetic fertilizers, this leads to a slow and steady release of nutrients that aren't just beneficial to the plants, but the entire ecosystem surrounding the plant.

Fine sand (play sand) Holds form better than coarse or sharp sand, but lowers the aeration of your soil mix which can hinder root penetration.

Grit/Crushed granite Excellent component for drastically increasing the drainage of your mix while adding plenty of aeration. Crushed granite is inert and doesn't break down. The size of particles used should be selected depending on the size of the plant and its root system. The smallest of particles function as useful anchors and support for seedlings.

LECA (Lightweight Expanded Clay Aggregates) These clay pellets are incredibly light and porous and are an idea medium used in hydroculture. This absorbent material soaks up excess water that is then transferred to dry particles, bringing water and moisture to the plant via capillary action.

Peat moss Slowly breaks down over time and increases the drainage of your soil mixture. Peat moss is also ideal for plants that prefer a lower PH.

Perlite Drastically increases drainage and aeration of your soil mixture and allows for better root penetration. Its light nature can cause smaller particles to migrate to the top of the pot overtime.

Pumice Virtually the same properties of perlite, but much heavier. In fact, perlite is just pumice thats been heated like popcorn. Pumice is less widely available and pricier, but a personal preference of mine. It also goes by dry stall and can be found at some agriculture stores.

Saw dust breaks down slowly and can add structure to your soil mixture. It can also be used to alter the PH of your mix depending on the source of the saw dust.

Vermiculite A sterile component that is ideal for young or sensitive plants. Vermiculite can lighten your soil mixture and improve drainage greatly. Its ideal for staving off fungal growth and bacteria that could otherwise thrive in your soil mixture.

Worm castings Contains a high yield of minerals. Worm Castings are a 100% organic fertilizer and can help retain moisture in your soil.

Understanding pH

The *pH* of your soil mixture can play a vital role in ensuring you grow the healthiest plants possible. There are a few factors that should be considered when experimenting with the pH of your soil, as not all plants are quite so picky-however that extra step towards understanding the specific needs of some plants could open up a whole new door for you in this hobby. The pH of your soil affects soil bacteria and bacterial growth, nutrient availability, and soil structure.

First, we need to understand what pH is.

pH is used to measure the concentration of hydrogen ions, which is to say evaluate the acidity or alkalinity of a solution or mixture. In your research, you may discover that some plants are quite particular when it comes to the pH of their home.

The pH scale ranges from 0 to 14, with 0 being most acidic, 14 being most alkaline; a neutral solution having a value of 7.

For those looking for an explanation to a seemingly arbitrary number, 7 is defined as the neutral middle point of the pH scale simply due to an agreed upon standard. At room temperature, H2O self ionizes a bit, producing Hydrogen and Hydroxide ions (both of which contribute to the acidity or alkalinity of a solution). Given these circumstances, the concentration of Hydrogen ions produced is about 10^-7. The same applies for Hydroxide ions. Given that the water in the example is completely neutral, 7 is given the value to represent neutrality.

Most plants will happily thrive and grow at or near a neutral pH (6-7.5) and actually prefer it (with a few exceptions).

Acidity

Plants that prefer an acidic soil will need a pH value under 7. Most acid loving plants won't require a pH under 5, and a bit of research will be necessary to determine whether or not your plant would thrive in an acidic environment.

If you find that lowering the pH of your soil will benefit the plant, a few things you can incorporate into your soil include: **elemental sulfur, aluminum sulfate, sphagnum peat, mulches, and iron sulfate.**

Alkalinity

Plants that prefer a more alkaline environment often don't require a pH higher than 8. Again, research will be required to determine whether or not your plants will thrive in an alkaline soil, but if you're hoping to raise the pH, some components you can work into your soil include: **lyme or powdered limestone and wood ash.**

Extensive research, notes and tips can be found in regards to most cultivated varieties and their pH preference. Dig deep and make sure any alterations to your soil's pH will benefit the plant. Care and extra thought should be taken with a potted plant as opposed to a garden bed or a plant placed in the ground.

I would also advise against haphazardly tossing handfuls of these components into your mix. Be mindful, take notes, and make observations on any changes before and after altering the pH- for your benefit and for the benefit of other growers that could learn from your experiments.

How to Use this Book

We must look at *everything* that goes into a plant if we are to understand their needs. This includes the soil used, where the plant was purchased, seasonal observations, and so on. This journal is laid out in such a way as to encourage those observations- requiring the reader and grower to be mindful of the transitions our plants make through their seasons and even encouraging growers to sketch their plants in varying detail—do it, even if you're horrible at drawing, and you'll get better at two things at once!

A hallmark of a good grower is attentiveness. My hope is this journal will help you focus in on your plants and better understand them through organized note-taking and excited observation. If these are traits you already possess towards your green friends, perhaps this journal will serve as a series of landing pages for the seasoned grower as well.

Fill out as many prompts and sections as possible throughout your journal, mark which plants are on which pages in the index so you can find them later, and take a metaphorical or literal magnifying lens to your green friends. You'll have a deeper understanding and appreciation for the things with which we fill our homes, gardens, and lives.

Entry Index

PAGE		PAGE	
22		174	
24		176	
26		178	
28		180	
30		182	
32		184	
34		186	
36		188	
38		190	
40		192	
42		194	
44		196	
46		198	
48		200	
50		202	
52		204	
54		206	
56		208	
58		210	
60		212	
62		214	
64		216	
66		218	
68		220	
70		222	
72		224	

FAMILY	Aizoaceae
GENUS	Lithops
SPECIES	otzeniana 'aquamarine'

DATE OF ENTRY

ACQUIRED FROM

○ SEED GROWN	X PURCHASED	○ CUTTING	○ FIELD COLLECTED
Date Sown	Supplier & Location MESA GARDEN		Date & Location: Did you do this sh*t ethically?

SOIL RECIPE "MESEMB MIX"

2 parts fine pumice, 1 part coco coir, 1 part coarse sand
.5 parts sifted compost

FERTILIZER REGIMEN

FERTILIZE WITH 10-10-10 at 1/10 concentration at beginning of growing SEASON

Amount of Water (X marked on second symbol)

Amount of Light (X marked on fourth symbol)

NOTES

* THESE PLANTS REQUIRE A SUMMER DORMANCY!
- If kept on the drier side, otzeniana are known for their sunken and excavated windows
- too much water will plump them up, removing this distinguishing and interesting feature.

Known Pests
~~Root~~ Mealy

Natural Habitat
ca 5 km N of Karasburg

Best Cultivation Environment
Dry w/ cool nights

Why/How I haplessly MURDERED this plant:
Squirrels ☹

SEASONAL OBSERVATIONS

	SPRING	SUMMER	AUTUMN	WINTER
Year One	- new leaves have emerged! - responds well to watering	- growing has ceased. - should not water too much.	flowers are emerging! - watering is resumed.	- growth has ceased, but new leaves are splitting through.
Year Two	- Same as year one!	dormancy seems to be a month late.	~~Both~~ heads flowered! - also seed pods are ripe	Splitting has begun. - now has 4 heads.

SKETCHES

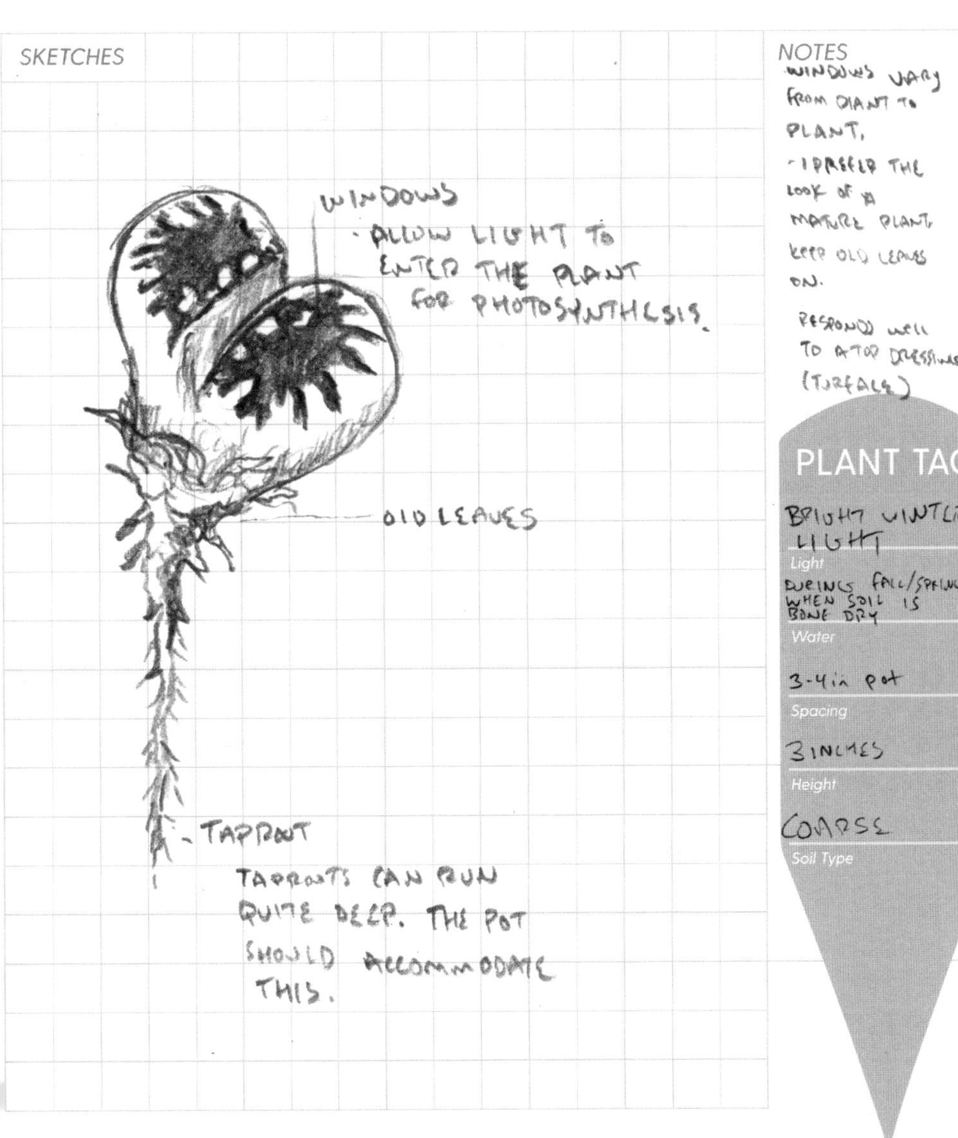

NOTES

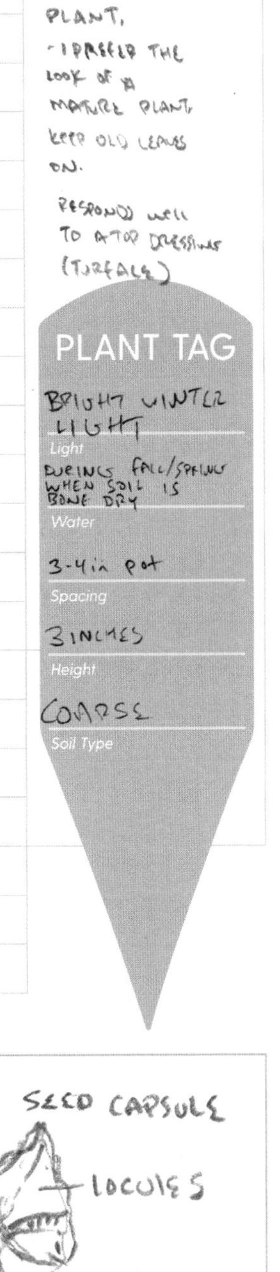

DETAIL 1

DETAIL 2

FAMILY	Crassulaceae
GENUS	Sedum
SPECIES	Sempervivoideae

DATE OF ENTRY

Jun, 8

6-8-23

ACQUIRED FROM

SEED GROWN	PURCHASED	CUTTING	FIELD COLLECTED
Date Sown	Supplier & Location		Date & Location: Did you do this sh*t ethically?

SOIL RECIPE

FERTILIZER REGIMEN

Amount of Water

Amount of Light

NOTES

Known Pests

Natural Habitat

Best Cultivation Environment

Why/How I haplessly MURDERED this plant:

SEASONAL OBSERVATIONS

Year One

SPRING	SUMMER	AUTUMN	WINTER

Year Two

SPRING	SUMMER	AUTUMN	WINTER

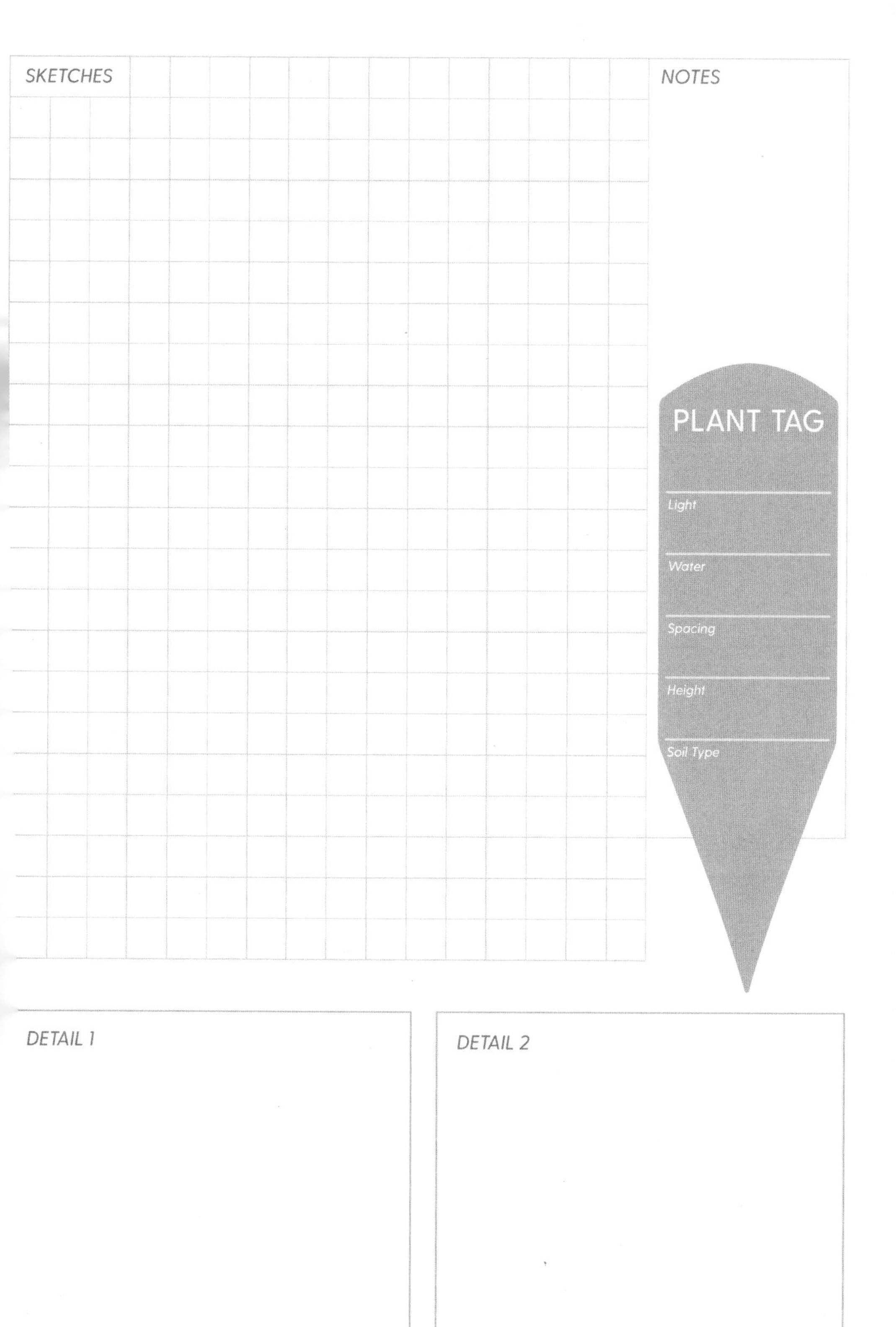
SKETCHES
NOTES
PLANT TAG
Light
Water
Spacing
Height
Soil Type
DETAIL 1
DETAIL 2

FAMILY

GENUS

SPECIES

DATE OF ENTRY

ACQUIRED FROM

SEED GROWN	PURCHASED	CUTTING	FIELD COLLECTED
Date Sown	Supplier & Location		Date & Location: Did you do this sh*t ethically?

SOIL RECIPE

FERTILIZER REGIMEN

Amount of Water

Amount of Light

NOTES

Known Pests

Natural Habitat

Best Cultivation Environment

Why/How I haplessly MURDERED this plant:

SEASONAL OBSERVATIONS

Year One	SPRING	SUMMER	AUTUMN	WINTER
Year Two	SPRING	SUMMER	AUTUMN	WINTER

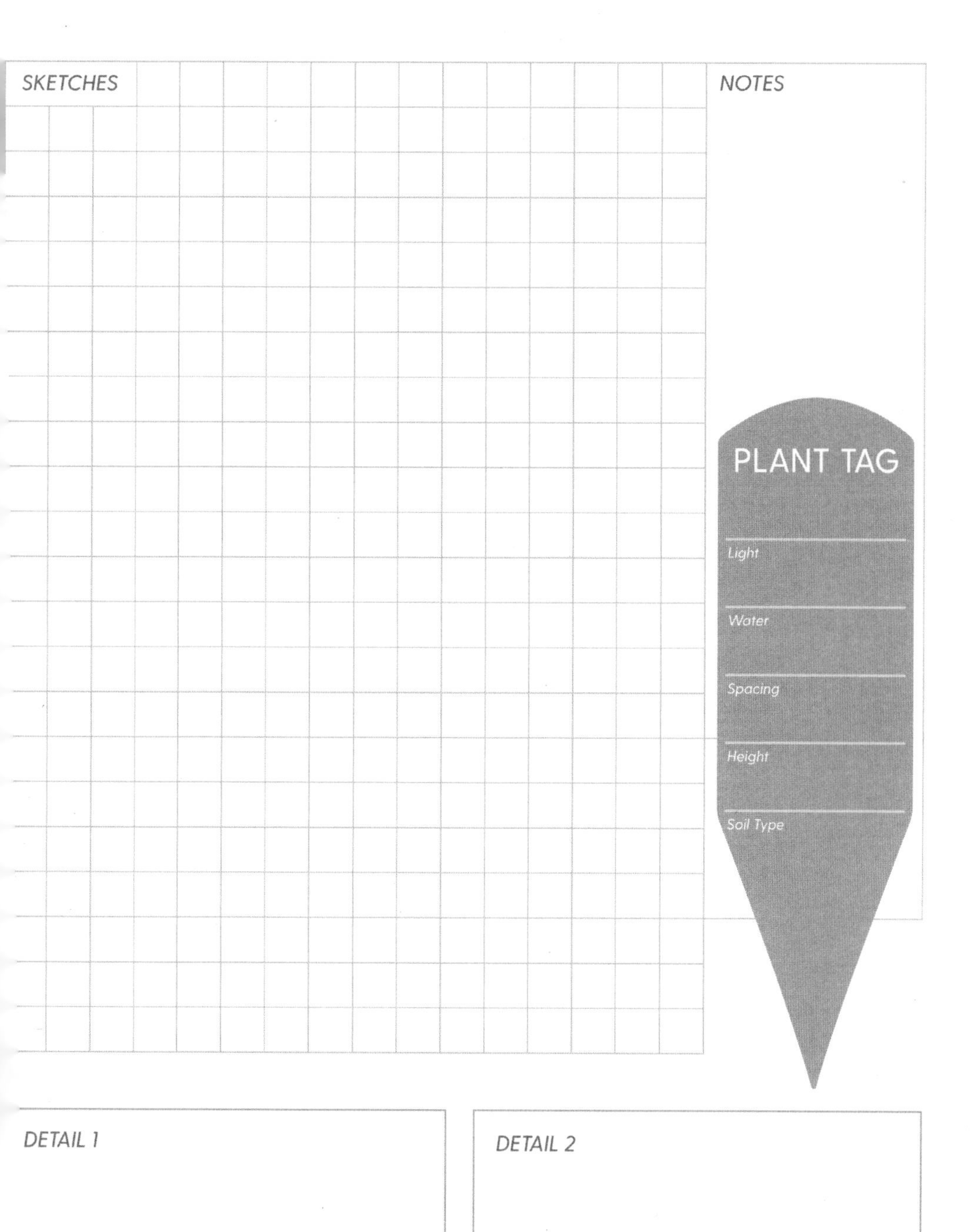

DETAIL 1

DETAIL 2

FAMILY

GENUS

SPECIES

DATE OF ENTRY

ACQUIRED FROM

SEED GROWN	PURCHASED	CUTTING	FIELD COLLECTED
Date Sown	Supplier & Location		Date & Location: Did you do this sh*t ethically?

SOIL RECIPE

FERTILIZER REGIMEN

Amount of Water

Amount of Light

NOTES

Known Pests

Natural Habitat

Best Cultivation Environment

Why/How I haplessly MURDERED this plant:

SEASONAL OBSERVATIONS

Year One

SPRING	SUMMER	AUTUMN	WINTER

Year Two

SPRING	SUMMER	AUTUMN	WINTER

SKETCHES

NOTES

PLANT TAG

Light

Water

Spacing

Height

Soil Type

DETAIL 1

DETAIL 2

FAMILY

GENUS

SPECIES

DATE OF ENTRY

ACQUIRED FROM

SEED GROWN	PURCHASED	CUTTING	FIELD COLLECTED
Date Sown	Supplier & Location		Date & Location: Did you do this sh*t ethically?

SOIL RECIPE

FERTILIZER REGIMEN

Amount of Water

Amount of Light

NOTES

Known Pests

Natural Habitat

Best Cultivation Environment

Why/How I haplessly MURDERED this plant:

SEASONAL OBSERVATIONS

Year One	SPRING	SUMMER	AUTUMN	WINTER
Year Two	SPRING	SUMMER	AUTUMN	WINTER

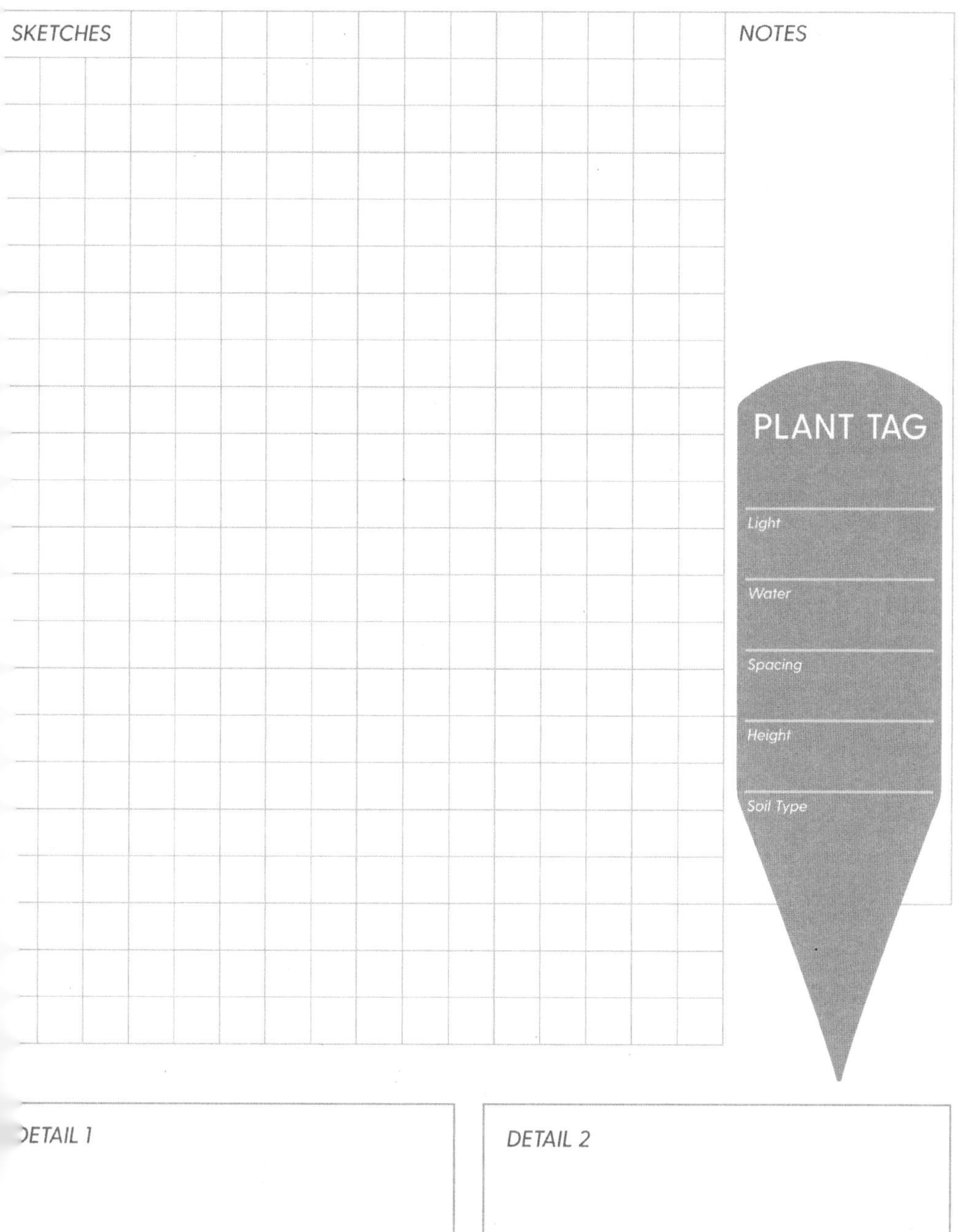

DETAIL 1

DETAIL 2

FAMILY

GENUS

SPECIES

DATE OF ENTRY

ACQUIRED FROM

SEED GROWN	PURCHASED	CUTTING	FIELD COLLECTED
Date Sown	Supplier & Location		Date & Location: Did you do this sh*t ethically?

SOIL RECIPE

FERTILIZER REGIMEN

Amount of Water

Amount of Light

NOTES

Known Pests

Natural Habitat

Best Cultivation Environment

Why/How I haplessly MURDERED this plant:

SEASONAL OBSERVATIONS

	SPRING	SUMMER	AUTUMN	WINTER
Year One				
Year Two				

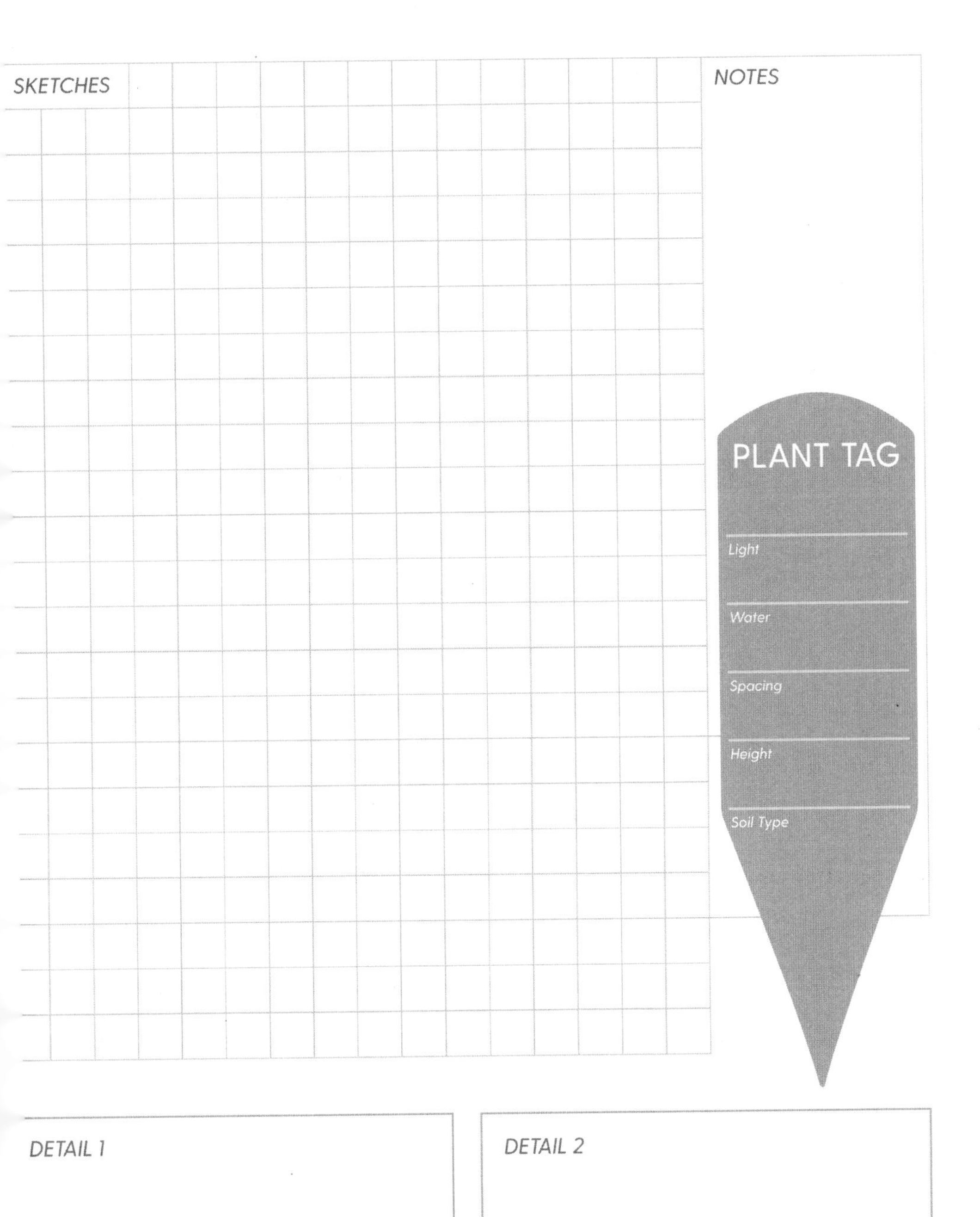

DETAIL 1

DETAIL 2

FAMILY

GENUS

SPECIES

DATE OF ENTRY

ACQUIRED FROM

SEED GROWN

Date Sown

PURCHASED

Supplier & Location

CUTTING

FIELD COLLECTED

Date & Location:

Did you do this sh*t ethically?

SOIL RECIPE

FERTILIZER REGIMEN

Amount of Water

Amount of Light

NOTES

Known Pests

Natural Habitat

Best Cultivation Environment

Why/How I haplessly MURDERED this plant:

SEASONAL OBSERVATIONS

Year One

SPRING	SUMMER	AUTUMN	WINTER

Year Two

SPRING	SUMMER	AUTUMN	WINTER

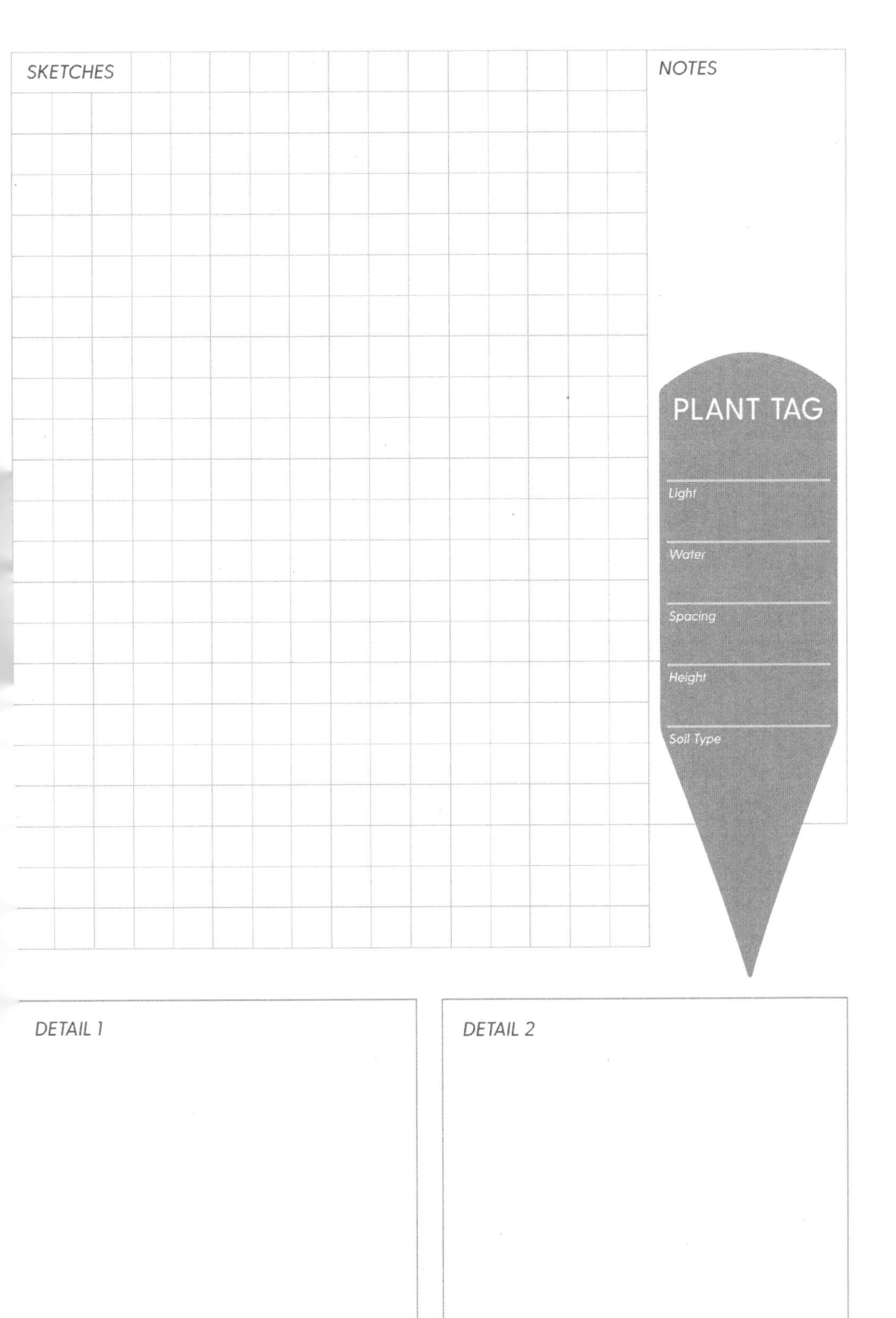
SKETCHES
NOTES
PLANT TAG
Light
Water
Spacing
Height
Soil Type
DETAIL 1
DETAIL 2

FAMILY

GENUS

SPECIES

DATE OF ENTRY

ACQUIRED FROM

SEED GROWN	PURCHASED	CUTTING	FIELD COLLECTED
Date Sown	Supplier & Location		Date & Location: Did you do this sh*t ethically?

SOIL RECIPE

FERTILIZER REGIMEN

Amount of Water

Amount of Light

NOTES

Known Pests

Natural Habitat

Best Cultivation Environment

Why/How I haplessly MURDERED this plant:

SEASONAL OBSERVATIONS

Year One	SPRING	SUMMER	AUTUMN	WINTER
Year Two	SPRING	SUMMER	AUTUMN	WINTER

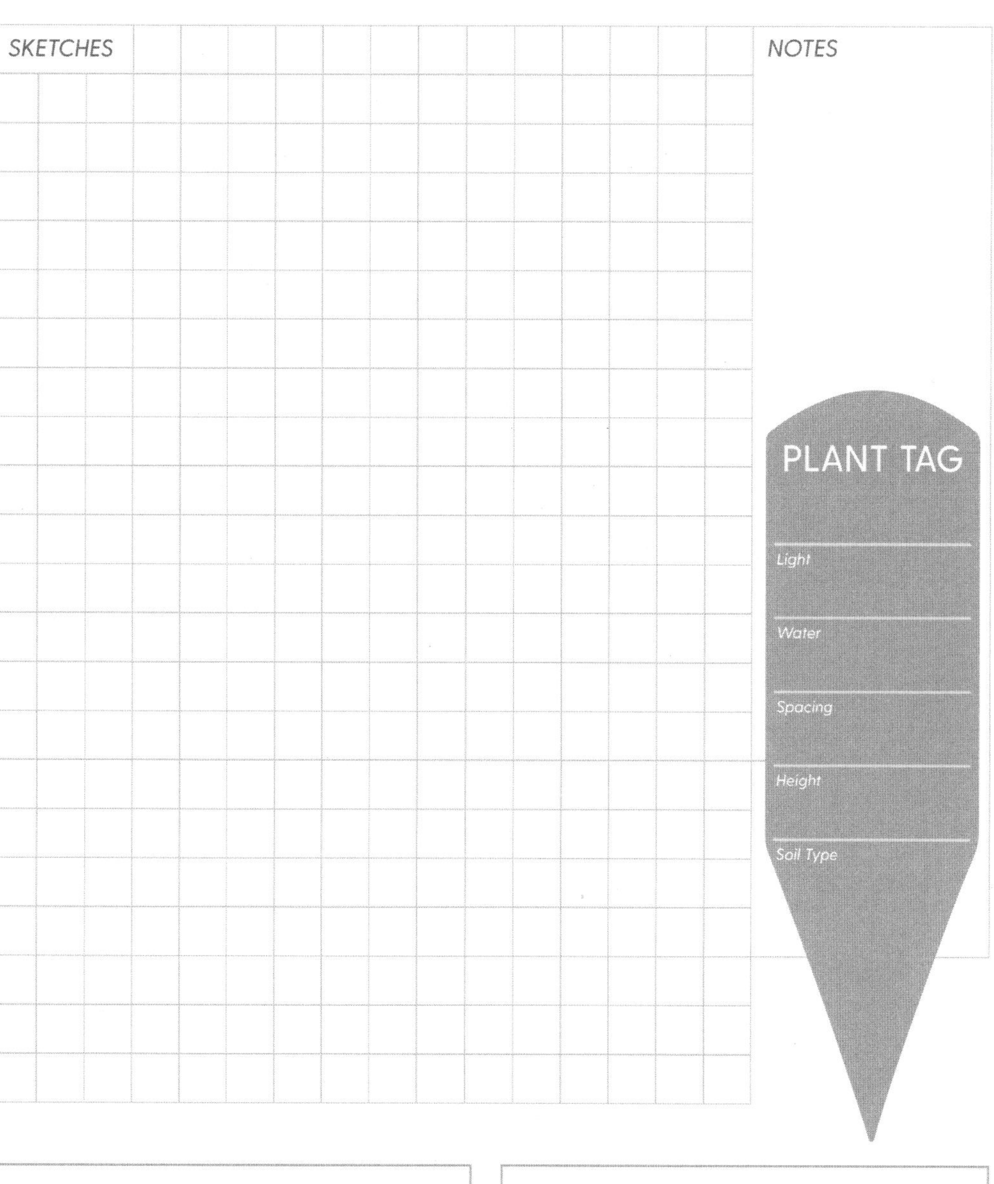

DETAIL 1

DETAIL 2

FAMILY

GENUS

SPECIES

DATE OF ENTRY

ACQUIRED FROM

SEED GROWN	PURCHASED	CUTTING	FIELD COLLECTED
Date Sown	Supplier & Location		Date & Location: Did you do this sh*t ethically?

SOIL RECIPE

FERTILIZER REGIMEN

Amount of Water

Amount of Light

NOTES

Known Pests

Natural Habitat

Best Cultivation Environment

Why/How I haplessly MURDERED this plant:

SEASONAL OBSERVATIONS

	SPRING	SUMMER	AUTUMN	WINTER
Year One				
Year Two				

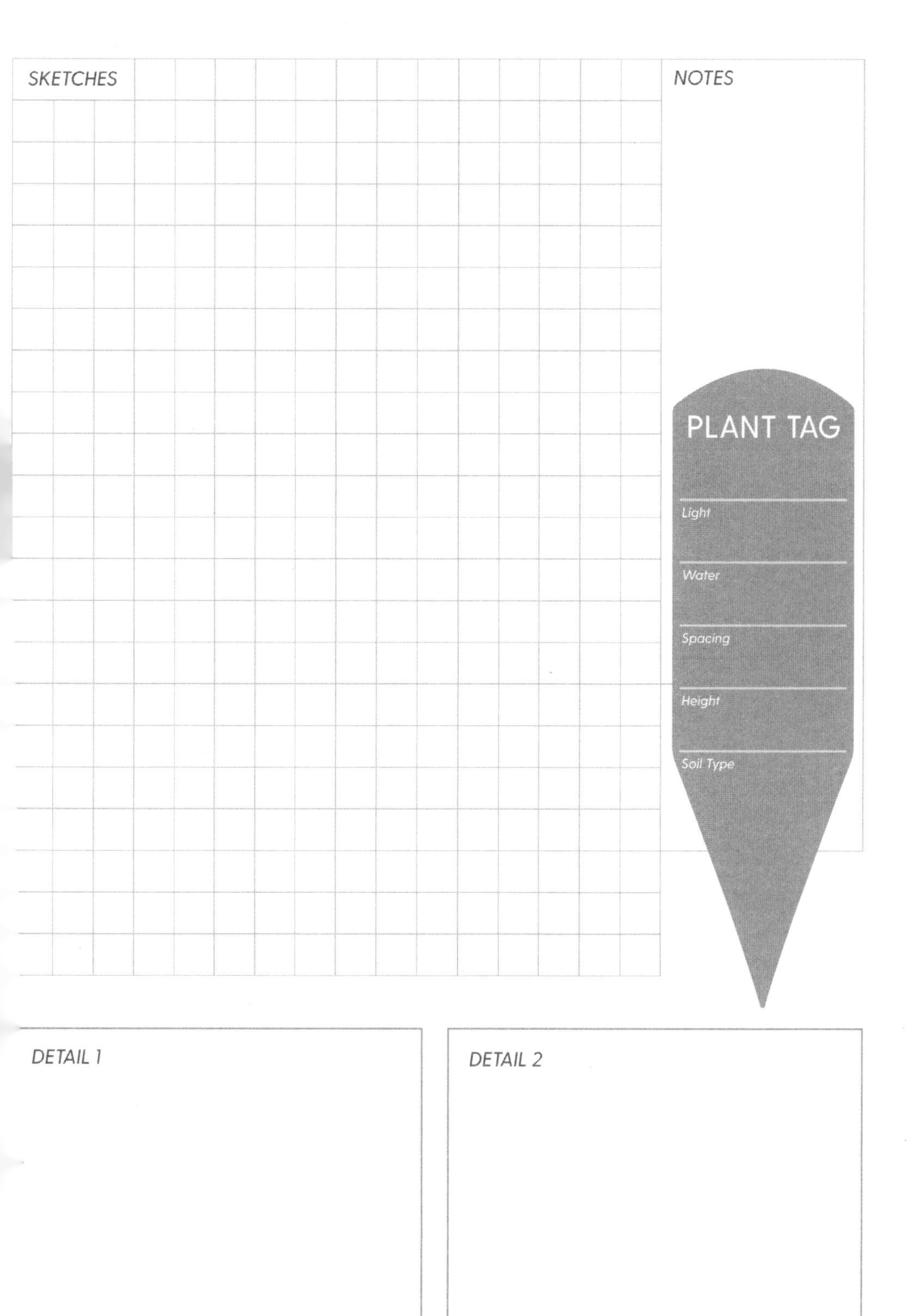

DETAIL 1

DETAIL 2

FAMILY

GENUS

SPECIES

DATE OF ENTRY

ACQUIRED FROM

SEED GROWN	PURCHASED	CUTTING	FIELD COLLECTED
Date Sown	Supplier & Location		Date & Location: Did you do this sh*t ethically?

SOIL RECIPE

FERTILIZER REGIMEN

Amount of Water

Amount of Light

NOTES

Known Pests

Natural Habitat

Best Cultivation Environment

Why/How I haplessly MURDERED this plant:

SEASONAL OBSERVATIONS

Year One

SPRING	SUMMER	AUTUMN	WINTER

Year Two

SPRING	SUMMER	AUTUMN	WINTER

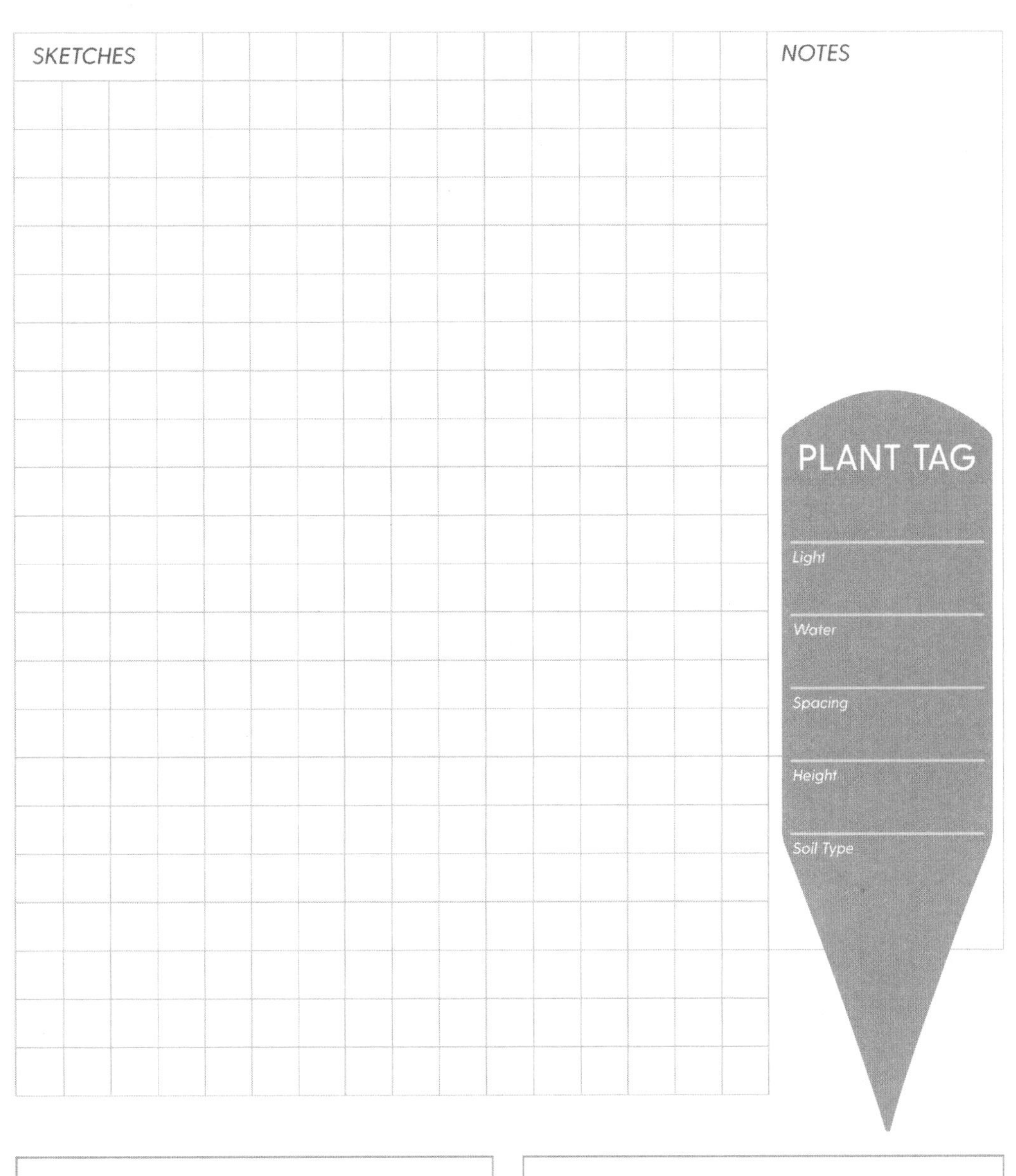

DETAIL 1

DETAIL 2

FAMILY	
GENUS	
SPECIES	

DATE OF ENTRY

ACQUIRED FROM

SEED GROWN	PURCHASED	CUTTING	FIELD COLLECTED
Date Sown	Supplier & Location		Date & Location: Did you do this sh*t ethically?

SOIL RECIPE

FERTILIZER REGIMEN

Amount of Water

Amount of Light

NOTES

Known Pests

Natural Habitat

Best Cultivation Environment

Why/How I haplessly MURDERED this plant:

SEASONAL OBSERVATIONS

Year One	SPRING	SUMMER	AUTUMN	WINTER
Year Two	SPRING	SUMMER	AUTUMN	WINTER

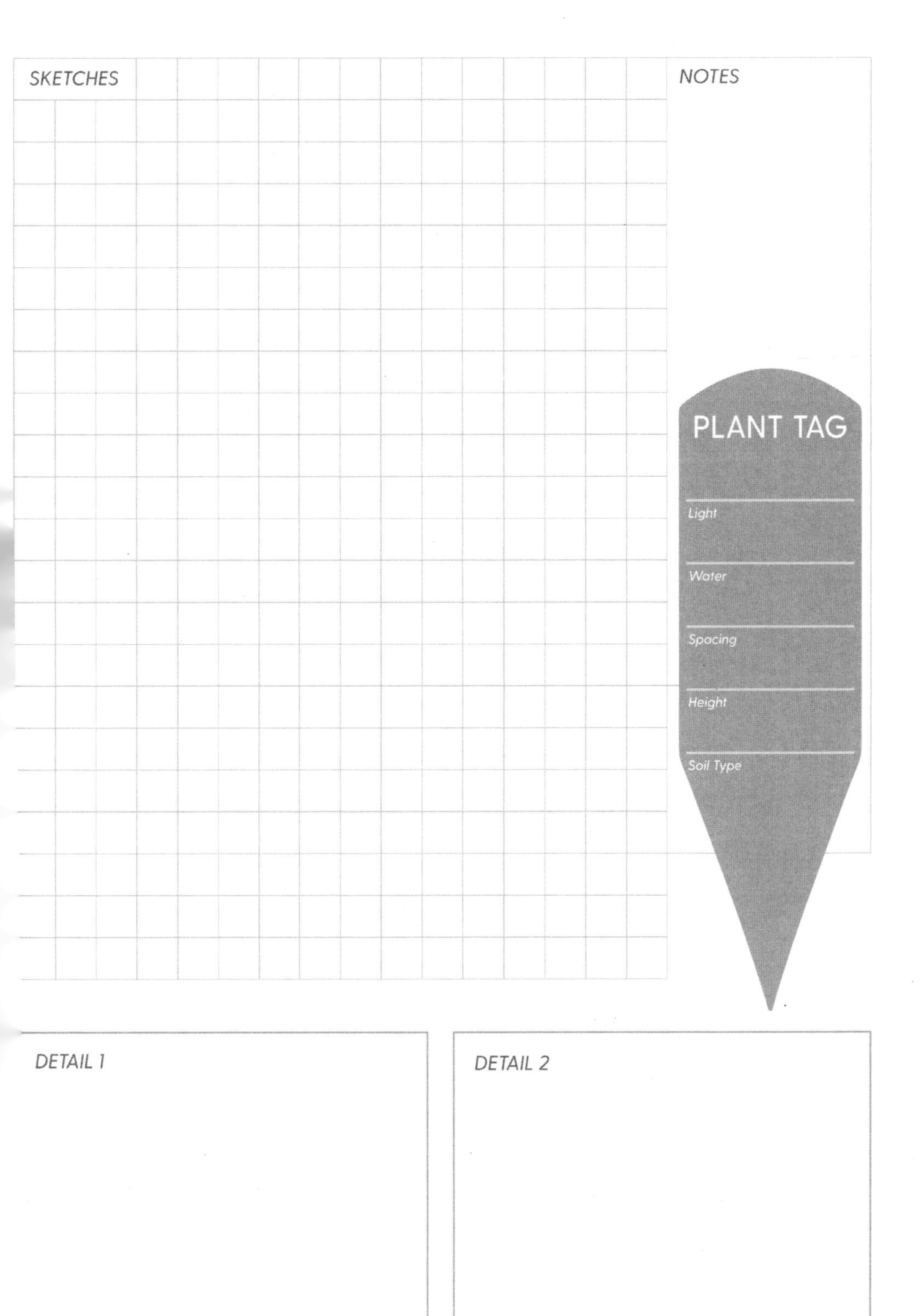

DETAIL 1

DETAIL 2

FAMILY

GENUS

SPECIES

DATE OF ENTRY

ACQUIRED FROM

SEED GROWN
Date Sown

PURCHASED
Supplier & Location

CUTTING

FIELD COLLECTED
Date & Location:
Did you do this sh*t ethically?

SOIL RECIPE

FERTILIZER REGIMEN

Amount of Water

Amount of Light

NOTES

Known Pests

Natural Habitat

Best Cultivation Environment

Why/How I haplessly MURDERED this plant:

SEASONAL OBSERVATIONS

Year One

SPRING	SUMMER	AUTUMN	WINTER

Year Two

SPRING	SUMMER	AUTUMN	WINTER

SKETCHES

NOTES

PLANT TAG

Light

Water

Spacing

Height

Soil Type

DETAIL 1

DETAIL 2

FAMILY

GENUS

SPECIES

DATE OF ENTRY

ACQUIRED FROM

SEED GROWN	PURCHASED	CUTTING	FIELD COLLECTED
Date Sown	Supplier & Location		Date & Location: Did you do this sh*t ethically?

SOIL RECIPE

FERTILIZER REGIMEN

Amount of Water

Amount of Light

NOTES

Known Pests

Natural Habitat

Best Cultivation Environment

Why/How I haplessly MURDERED this plant:

SEASONAL OBSERVATIONS

Year One

SPRING	SUMMER	AUTUMN	WINTER

Year Two

SPRING	SUMMER	AUTUMN	WINTER

SKETCHES

NOTES

PLANT TAG

Light

Water

Spacing

Height

Soil Type

DETAIL 1

DETAIL 2

FAMILY

GENUS

SPECIES

DATE OF ENTRY

ACQUIRED FROM

SEED GROWN

Date Sown

PURCHASED

Supplier & Location

CUTTING

FIELD COLLECTED

Date & Location:

Did you do this sh*t ethically?

SOIL RECIPE

FERTILIZER REGIMEN

Amount of Water

Amount of Light

NOTES

Known Pests

Natural Habitat

Best Cultivation Environment

Why/How I haplessly MURDERED this plant:

SEASONAL OBSERVATIONS

Year One

SPRING

SUMMER

AUTUMN

WINTER

Year Two

SPRING

SUMMER

AUTUMN

WINTER

SKETCHES

NOTES

PLANT TAG

Light

Water

Spacing

Height

Soil Type

DETAIL 1

DETAIL 2

FAMILY

GENUS

SPECIES

DATE OF ENTRY

ACQUIRED FROM

SEED GROWN	PURCHASED	CUTTING	FIELD COLLECTED
Date Sown	Supplier & Location		Date & Location: Did you do this sh*t ethically?

SOIL RECIPE

FERTILIZER REGIMEN

Amount of Water

Amount of Light

NOTES

Known Pests

Natural Habitat

Best Cultivation Environment

Why/How I haplessly MURDERED this plant:

SEASONAL OBSERVATIONS

Year One

SPRING	SUMMER	AUTUMN	WINTER

Year Two

SPRING	SUMMER	AUTUMN	WINTER

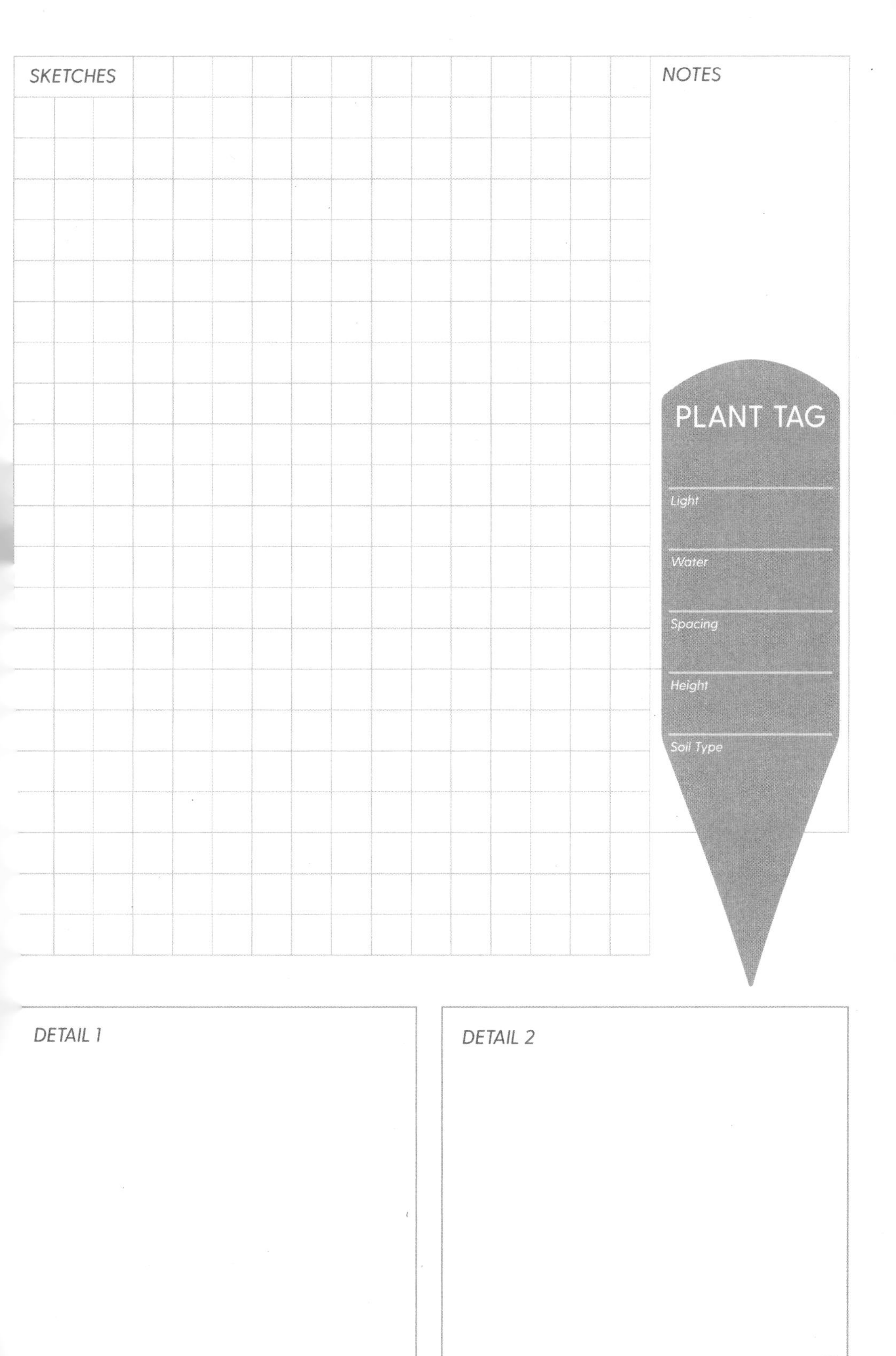
SKETCHES
NOTES
PLANT TAG
Light
Water
Spacing
Height
Soil Type
DETAIL 1
DETAIL 2

FAMILY

GENUS

SPECIES

DATE OF ENTRY

ACQUIRED FROM

SEED GROWN	PURCHASED	CUTTING	FIELD COLLECTED
Date Sown	Supplier & Location		Date & Location: Did you do this sh*t ethically?

SOIL RECIPE

FERTILIZER REGIMEN

Amount of Water

Amount of Light

NOTES

Known Pests

Natural Habitat

Best Cultivation Environment

Why/How I haplessly MURDERED this plant:

SEASONAL OBSERVATIONS

Year One	SPRING	SUMMER	AUTUMN	WINTER
Year Two	SPRING	SUMMER	AUTUMN	WINTER

SKETCHES

NOTES

PLANT TAG

Light

Water

Spacing

Height

Soil Type

DETAIL 1

DETAIL 2

FAMILY
GENUS
SPECIES

DATE OF ENTRY

ACQUIRED FROM

SEED GROWN	PURCHASED	CUTTING	FIELD COLLECTED
Date Sown	Supplier & Location		Date & Location: Did you do this sh*t ethically?

SOIL RECIPE

FERTILIZER REGIMEN

Amount of Water

Amount of Light

NOTES

Known Pests

Natural Habitat

Best Cultivation Environment

Why/How I haplessly MURDERED this plant:

SEASONAL OBSERVATIONS

Year One	SPRING	SUMMER	AUTUMN	WINTER
Year Two	SPRING	SUMMER	AUTUMN	WINTER

SKETCHES

NOTES

PLANT TAG

Light

Water

Spacing

Height

Soil Type

DETAIL 1

DETAIL 2

FAMILY

GENUS

SPECIES

DATE OF ENTRY

ACQUIRED FROM

SEED GROWN	PURCHASED	CUTTING	FIELD COLLECTED
Date Sown	Supplier & Location		Date & Location: Did you do this sh*t ethically?

SOIL RECIPE

FERTILIZER REGIMEN

Amount of Water

Amount of Light

NOTES

Known Pests

Natural Habitat

Best Cultivation Environment

Why/How I haplessly MURDERED this plant:

SEASONAL OBSERVATIONS

Year One

SPRING	SUMMER	AUTUMN	WINTER

Year Two

SPRING	SUMMER	AUTUMN	WINTER

SKETCHES

NOTES

PLANT TAG

Light

Water

Spacing

Height

Soil Type

DETAIL 1

DETAIL 2

FAMILY

GENUS

SPECIES

DATE OF ENTRY

ACQUIRED FROM

SEED GROWN

Date Sown

PURCHASED

Supplier & Location

CUTTING

FIELD COLLECTED

Date & Location:

Did you do this sh*t ethically?

SOIL RECIPE

FERTILIZER REGIMEN

Amount of Water

Amount of Light

NOTES

Known Pests

Natural Habitat

Best Cultivation Environment

Why/How I haplessly MURDERED this plant:

SEASONAL OBSERVATIONS

Year One

SPRING

SUMMER

AUTUMN

WINTER

Year Two

SPRING

SUMMER

AUTUMN

WINTER

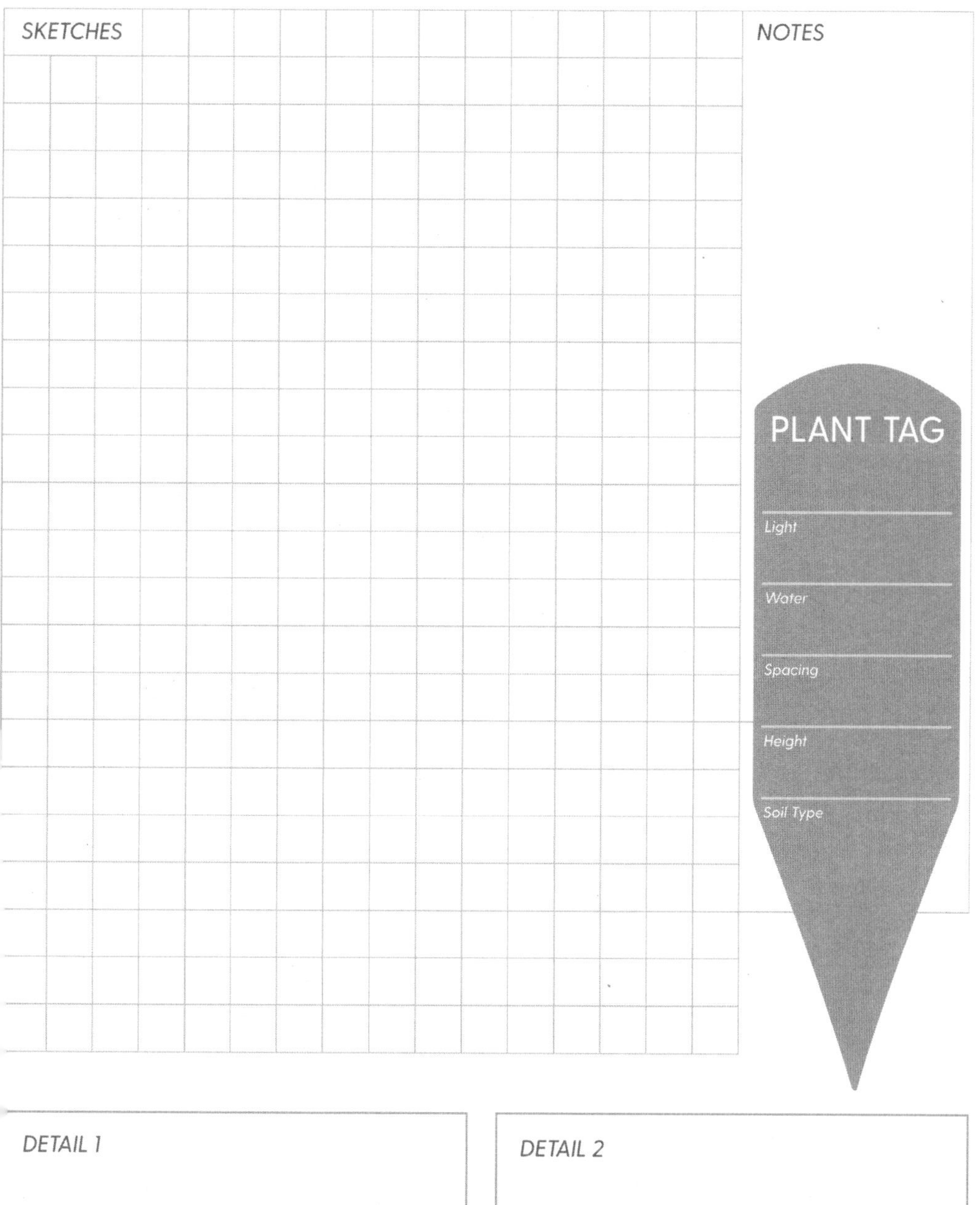

DETAIL 1

DETAIL 2

FAMILY	
GENUS	
SPECIES	

DATE OF ENTRY

ACQUIRED FROM

SEED GROWN	PURCHASED	CUTTING	FIELD COLLECTED
Date Sown	Supplier & Location		Date & Location: Did you do this sh*t ethically?

SOIL RECIPE

FERTILIZER REGIMEN

Amount of Water

Amount of Light

NOTES

Known Pests

Natural Habitat

Best Cultivation Environment

Why/How I haplessly MURDERED this plant:

SEASONAL OBSERVATIONS

	SPRING	SUMMER	AUTUMN	WINTER
Year One				
Year Two				

SKETCHES

NOTES

PLANT TAG

Light

Water

Spacing

Height

Soil Type

DETAIL 1

DETAIL 2

FAMILY

GENUS

SPECIES

DATE OF ENTRY

ACQUIRED FROM

SEED GROWN	PURCHASED	CUTTING	FIELD COLLECTED
Date Sown	Supplier & Location		Date & Location: Did you do this sh*t ethically?

SOIL RECIPE

FERTILIZER REGIMEN

Amount of Water

Amount of Light

NOTES

Known Pests

Natural Habitat

Best Cultivation Environment

Why/How I haplessly MURDERED this plant:

SEASONAL OBSERVATIONS

Year One	SPRING	SUMMER	AUTUMN	WINTER
Year Two	SPRING	SUMMER	AUTUMN	WINTER

SKETCHES

NOTES

PLANT TAG

Light

Water

Spacing

Height

Soil Type

DETAIL 1

DETAIL 2

FAMILY

GENUS

SPECIES

DATE OF ENTRY

ACQUIRED FROM

SEED GROWN	PURCHASED	CUTTING	FIELD COLLECTED
Date Sown	Supplier & Location		Date & Location: Did you do this sh*t ethically?

SOIL RECIPE

FERTILIZER REGIMEN

Amount of Water

Amount of Light

NOTES

Known Pests

Natural Habitat

Best Cultivation Environment

Why/How I haplessly MURDERED this plant:

SEASONAL OBSERVATIONS

Year One

SPRING	SUMMER	AUTUMN	WINTER

Year Two

SPRING	SUMMER	AUTUMN	WINTER

SKETCHES

NOTES

PLANT TAG

Light

Water

Spacing

Height

Soil Type

DETAIL 1

DETAIL 2

FAMILY

GENUS

SPECIES

DATE OF ENTRY

ACQUIRED FROM

SEED GROWN	PURCHASED	CUTTING	FIELD COLLECTED
Date Sown	Supplier & Location		Date & Location: Did you do this sh*t ethically?

SOIL RECIPE

FERTILIZER REGIMEN

Amount of Water

Amount of Light

NOTES

Known Pests

Natural Habitat

Best Cultivation Environment

Why/How I haplessly MURDERED this plant:

SEASONAL OBSERVATIONS

Year One

SPRING	SUMMER	AUTUMN	WINTER

Year Two

SPRING	SUMMER	AUTUMN	WINTER

SKETCHES

NOTES

PLANT TAG

Light

Water

Spacing

Height

Soil Type

DETAIL 1

DETAIL 2

FAMILY

GENUS

SPECIES

DATE OF ENTRY

ACQUIRED FROM

SEED GROWN	PURCHASED	CUTTING	FIELD COLLECTED
Date Sown	Supplier & Location		Date & Location: Did you do this sh*t ethically?

SOIL RECIPE

FERTILIZER REGIMEN

Amount of Water

Amount of Light

NOTES

Known Pests

Natural Habitat

Best Cultivation Environment

Why/How I haplessly MURDERED this plant:

SEASONAL OBSERVATIONS

Year One

SPRING	SUMMER	AUTUMN	WINTER

Year Two

SPRING	SUMMER	AUTUMN	WINTER

SKETCHES

NOTES

PLANT TAG

Light

Water

Spacing

Height

Soil Type

DETAIL 1

DETAIL 2

FAMILY

GENUS

SPECIES

DATE OF ENTRY

ACQUIRED FROM

SEED GROWN	PURCHASED	CUTTING	FIELD COLLECTED
Date Sown	Supplier & Location		Date & Location: Did you do this sh*t ethically?

SOIL RECIPE

FERTILIZER REGIMEN

Amount of Water

Amount of Light

NOTES

Known Pests

Natural Habitat

Best Cultivation Environment

Why/How I haplessly MURDERED this plant:

SEASONAL OBSERVATIONS

Year One	SPRING	SUMMER	AUTUMN	WINTER
Year Two	SPRING	SUMMER	AUTUMN	WINTER

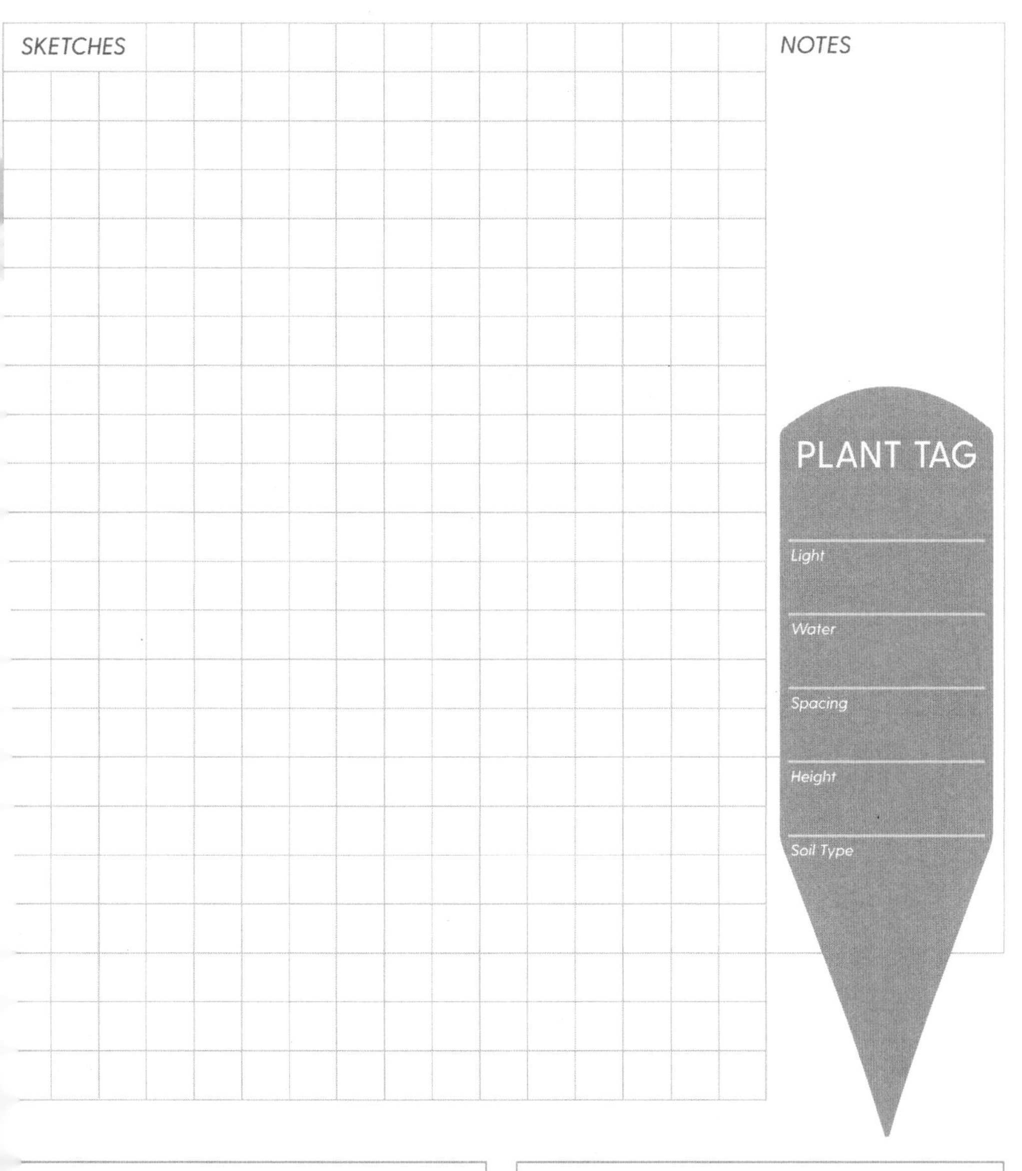

DETAIL 1

DETAIL 2

FAMILY

GENUS

SPECIES

DATE OF ENTRY

ACQUIRED FROM

SEED GROWN	PURCHASED	CUTTING	FIELD COLLECTED
Date Sown	Supplier & Location		Date & Location: Did you do this sh*t ethically?

SOIL RECIPE

FERTILIZER REGIMEN

Amount of Water

Amount of Light

NOTES

Known Pests

Natural Habitat

Best Cultivation Environment

Why/How I haplessly MURDERED this plant:

SEASONAL OBSERVATIONS

Year One

SPRING	SUMMER	AUTUMN	WINTER

Year Two

SPRING	SUMMER	AUTUMN	WINTER

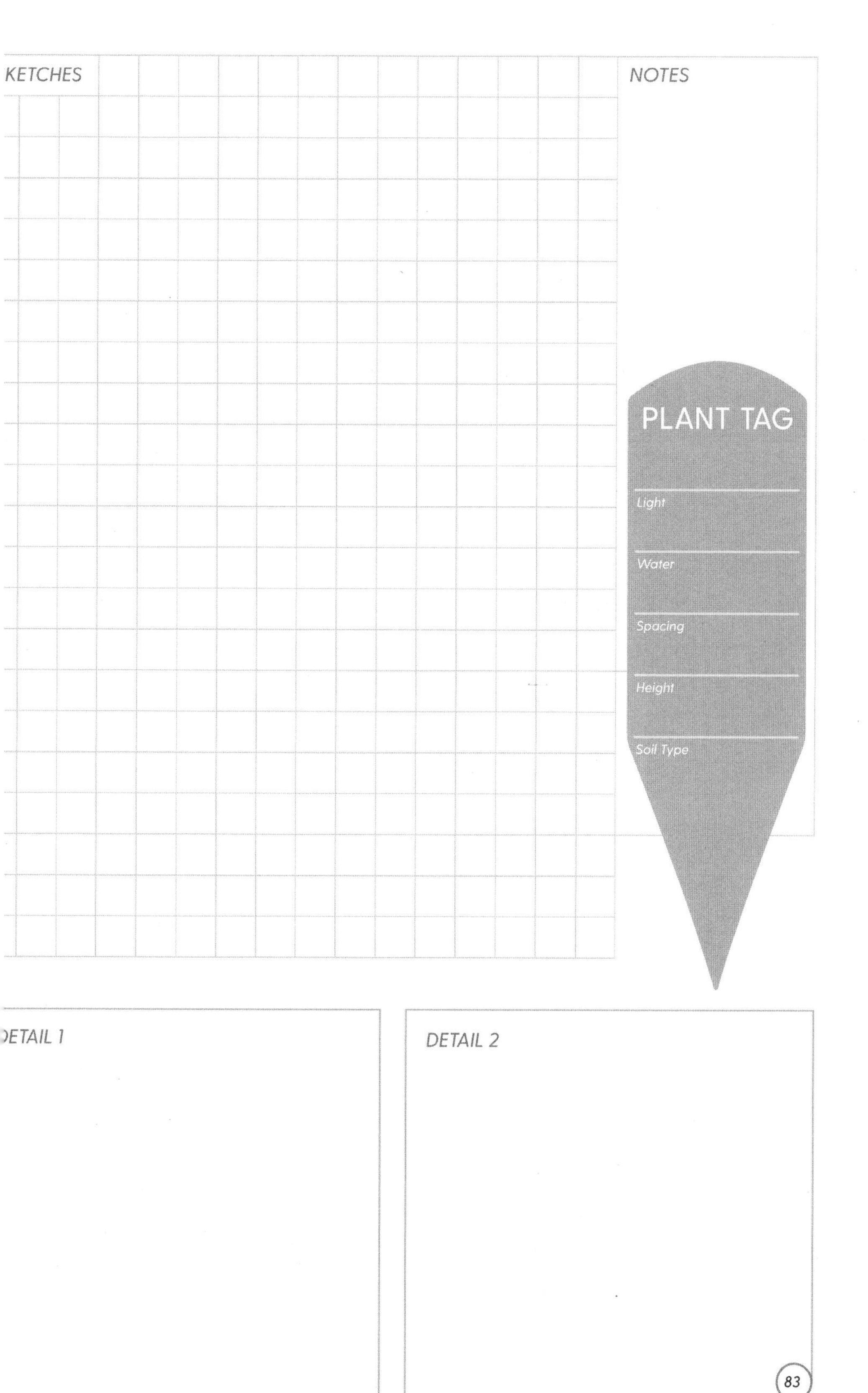
KETCHES
NOTES
PLANT TAG
Light
Water
Spacing
Height
Soil Type
DETAIL 1
DETAIL 2

FAMILY

GENUS

SPECIES

DATE OF ENTRY

ACQUIRED FROM

SEED GROWN	PURCHASED	CUTTING	FIELD COLLECTED
Date Sown	Supplier & Location		Date & Location: Did you do this sh*t ethically?

SOIL RECIPE

FERTILIZER REGIMEN

Amount of Water

Amount of Light

NOTES

Known Pests

Natural Habitat

Best Cultivation Environment

Why/How I haplessly MURDERED this plant:

SEASONAL OBSERVATIONS

Year One	SPRING	SUMMER	AUTUMN	WINTER
Year Two	SPRING	SUMMER	AUTUMN	WINTER

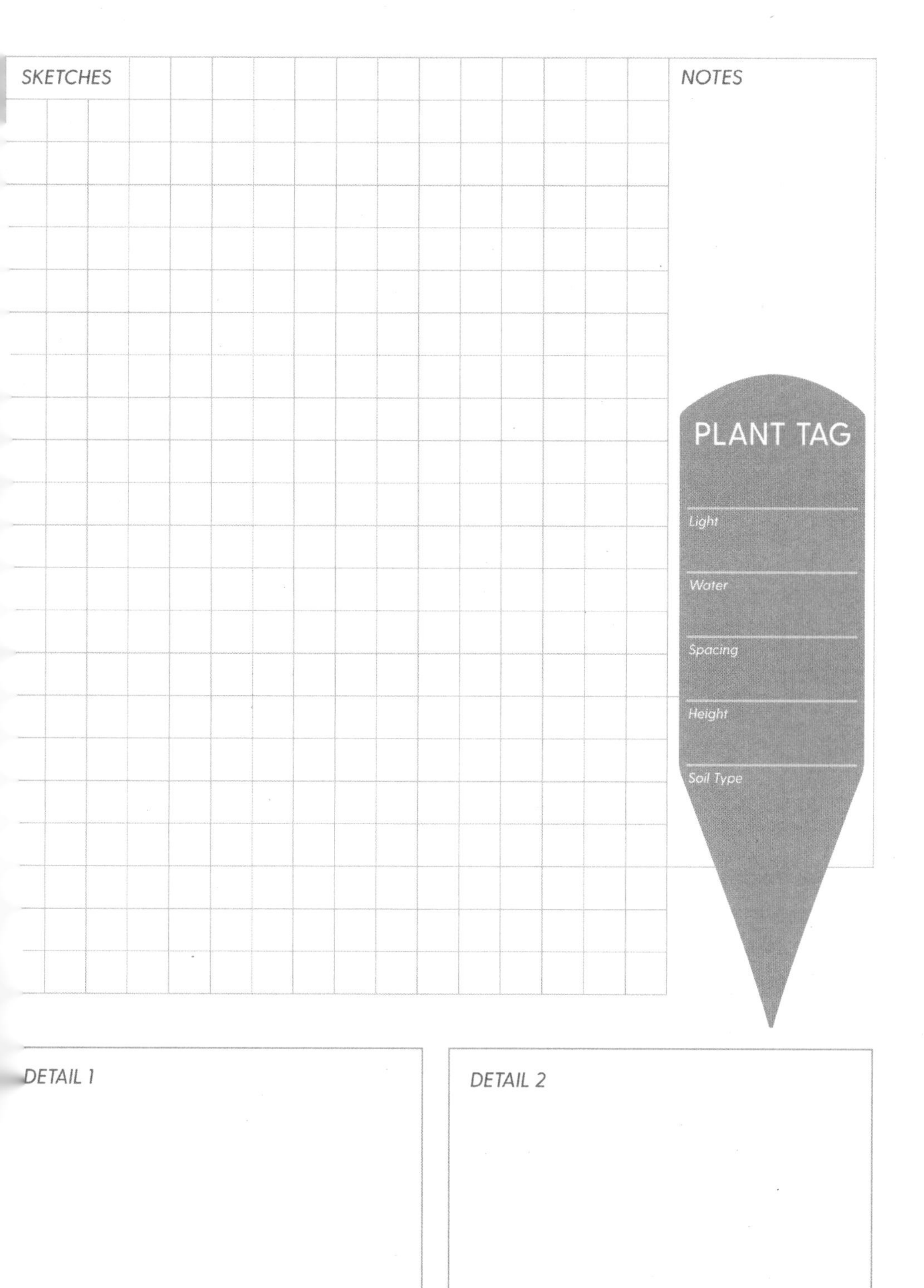

DETAIL 1

DETAIL 2

FAMILY

GENUS

SPECIES

DATE OF ENTRY

ACQUIRED FROM

SEED GROWN	PURCHASED	CUTTING	FIELD COLLECTED
Date Sown	Supplier & Location		Date & Location: Did you do this sh*t ethically?

SOIL RECIPE

FERTILIZER REGIMEN

Amount of Water

Amount of Light

NOTES

Known Pests

Natural Habitat

Best Cultivation Environment

Why/How I haplessly MURDERED this plant:

SEASONAL OBSERVATIONS

Year One

SPRING	SUMMER	AUTUMN	WINTER

Year Two

SPRING	SUMMER	AUTUMN	WINTER

SKETCHES

NOTES

PLANT TAG

Light

Water

Spacing

Height

Soil Type

DETAIL 1

DETAIL 2

FAMILY

GENUS

SPECIES

DATE OF ENTRY

ACQUIRED FROM

SEED GROWN	PURCHASED	CUTTING	FIELD COLLECTED
Date Sown	Supplier & Location		Date & Location: Did you do this sh*t ethically?

SOIL RECIPE

FERTILIZER REGIMEN

Amount of Water

Amount of Light

NOTES

Known Pests

Natural Habitat

Best Cultivation Environment

Why/How I haplessly MURDERED this plant:

SEASONAL OBSERVATIONS

Year One

SPRING	SUMMER	AUTUMN	WINTER

Year Two

SPRING	SUMMER	AUTUMN	WINTER

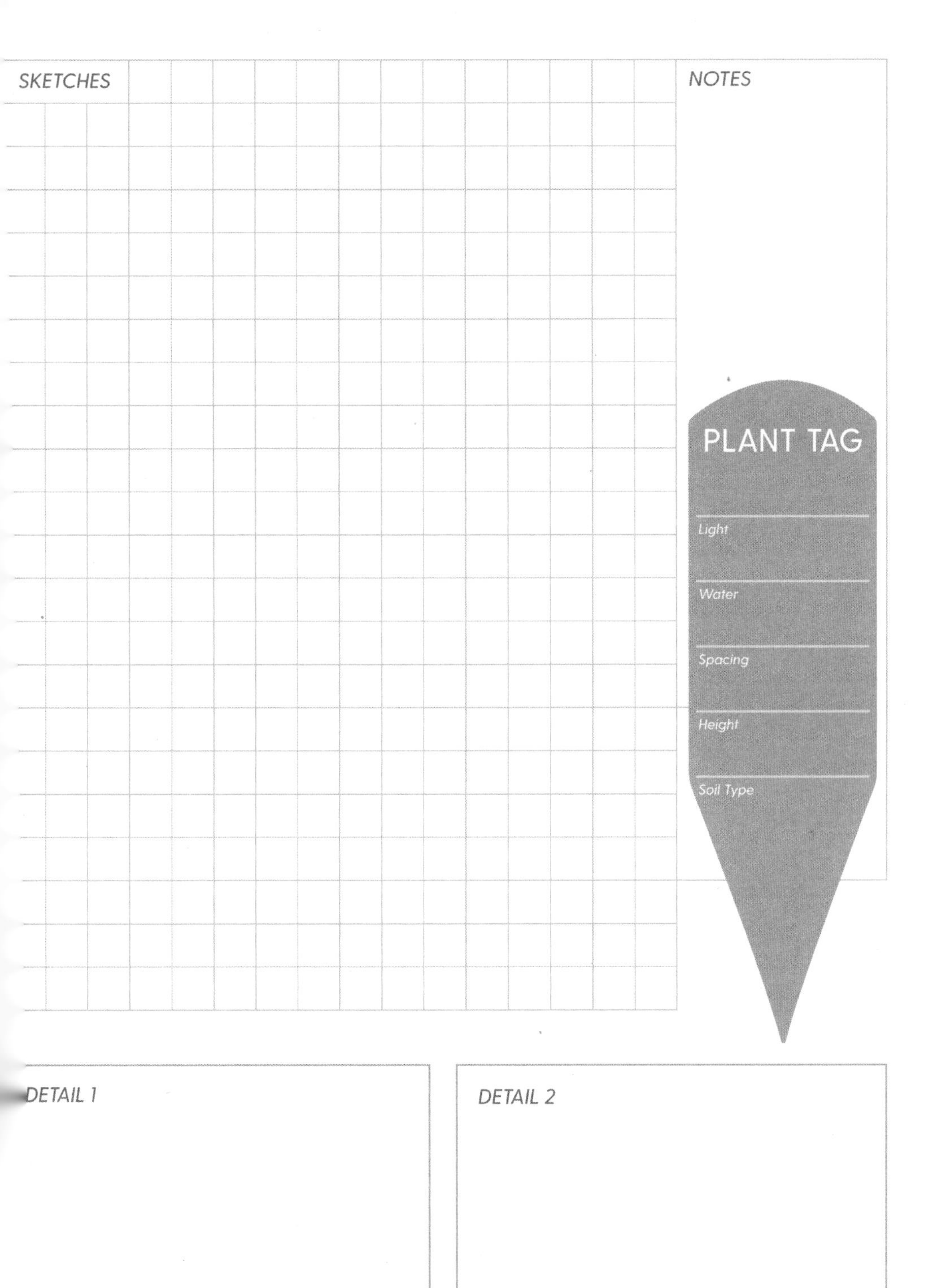

DETAIL 1

DETAIL 2

FAMILY

GENUS

SPECIES

DATE OF ENTRY

ACQUIRED FROM

SEED GROWN	PURCHASED	CUTTING	FIELD COLLECTED
Date Sown	Supplier & Location		Date & Location: Did you do this sh*t ethically?

SOIL RECIPE

FERTILIZER REGIMEN

Amount of Water

Amount of Light

NOTES

Known Pests

Natural Habitat

Best Cultivation Environment

Why/How I haplessly MURDERED this plant:

SEASONAL OBSERVATIONS

Year One

SPRING	SUMMER	AUTUMN	WINTER

Year Two

SPRING	SUMMER	AUTUMN	WINTER

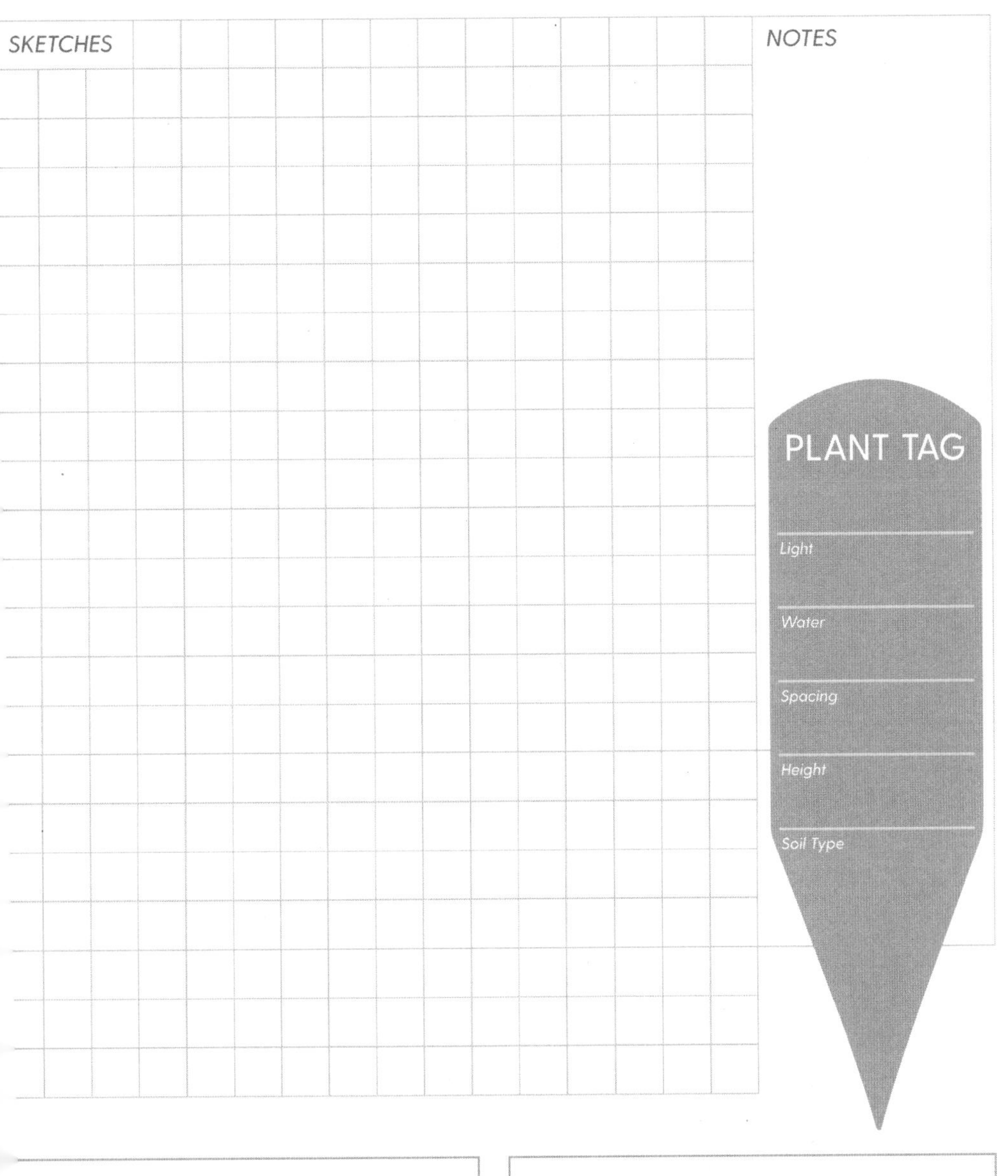

DETAIL 1

DETAIL 2

FAMILY

GENUS

SPECIES

DATE OF ENTRY

ACQUIRED FROM

SEED GROWN	PURCHASED	CUTTING	FIELD COLLECTED
Date Sown	Supplier & Location		Date & Location: Did you do this sh*t ethically?

SOIL RECIPE

FERTILIZER REGIMEN

Amount of Water

Amount of Light

NOTES

Known Pests

Natural Habitat

Best Cultivation Environment

Why/How I haplessly MURDERED this plant:

SEASONAL OBSERVATIONS

Year One	SPRING	SUMMER	AUTUMN	WINTER
Year Two	SPRING	SUMMER	AUTUMN	WINTER

SKETCHES

NOTES

PLANT TAG

Light

Water

Spacing

Height

Soil Type

DETAIL 1

DETAIL 2

FAMILY

GENUS

SPECIES

DATE OF ENTRY

ACQUIRED FROM

SEED GROWN	PURCHASED	CUTTING	FIELD COLLECTED
Date Sown	Supplier & Location		Date & Location: Did you do this sh*t ethically?

SOIL RECIPE

FERTILIZER REGIMEN

Amount of Water

Amount of Light

NOTES

Known Pests

Natural Habitat

Best Cultivation Environment

Why/How I haplessly MURDERED this plant:

SEASONAL OBSERVATIONS

Year One	SPRING	SUMMER	AUTUMN	WINTER
Year Two	SPRING	SUMMER	AUTUMN	WINTER

SKETCHES

NOTES

PLANT TAG

Light

Water

Spacing

Height

Soil Type

DETAIL 1

DETAIL 2

FAMILY

GENUS

SPECIES

DATE OF ENTRY

ACQUIRED FROM

SEED GROWN	PURCHASED	CUTTING	FIELD COLLECTED
Date Sown	Supplier & Location		Date & Location: Did you do this sh*t ethically?

SOIL RECIPE

FERTILIZER REGIMEN

Amount of Water

Amount of Light

NOTES

Known Pests

Natural Habitat

Best Cultivation Environment

Why/How I haplessly MURDERED this plant:

SEASONAL OBSERVATIONS

Year One

SPRING	SUMMER	AUTUMN	WINTER

Year Two

SPRING	SUMMER	AUTUMN	WINTER

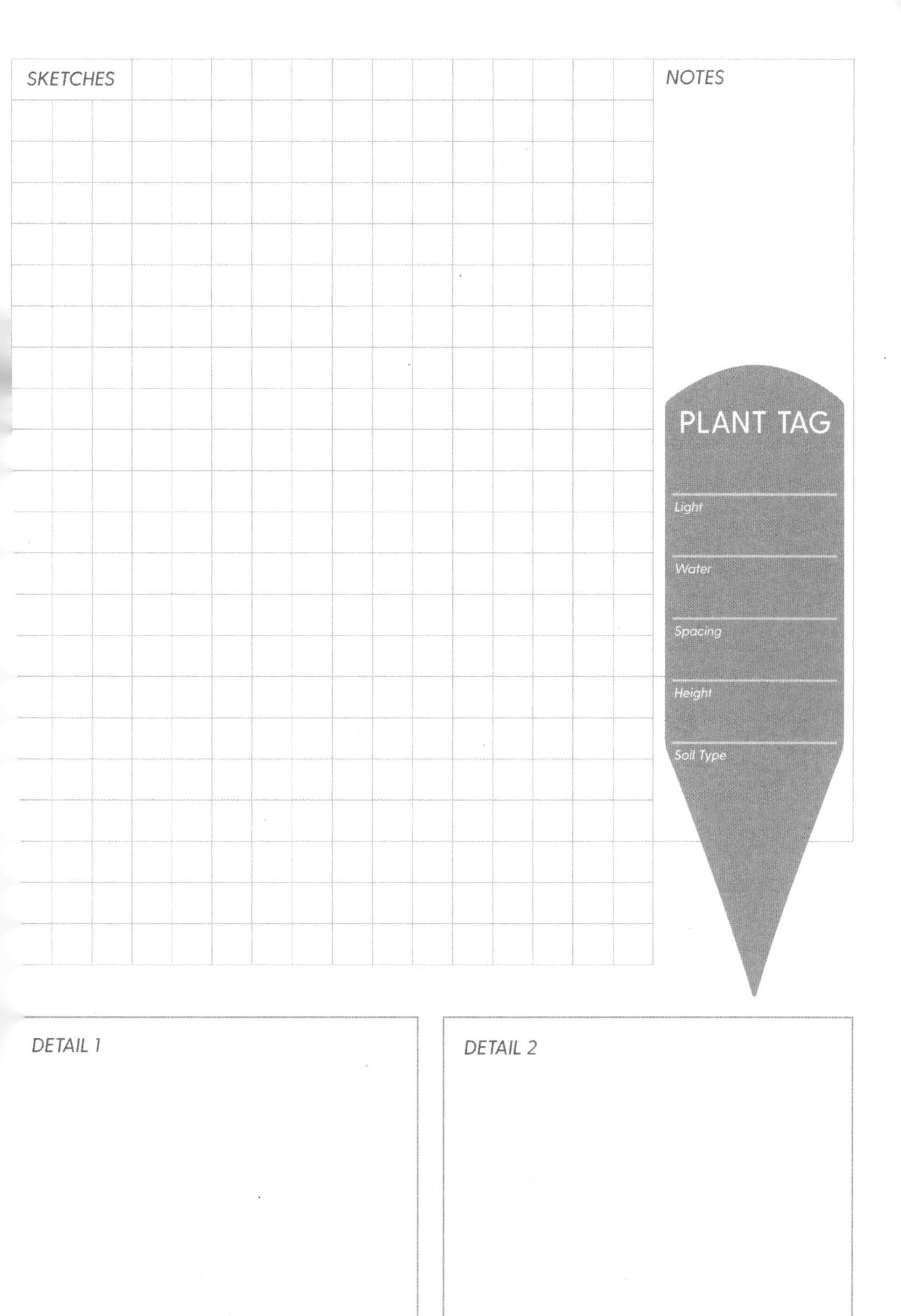

DETAIL 1

DETAIL 2

FAMILY

GENUS

SPECIES

DATE OF ENTRY

ACQUIRED FROM

SEED GROWN

Date Sown

PURCHASED

Supplier & Location

CUTTING

FIELD COLLECTED

Date & Location:

Did you do this sh*t ethically?

SOIL RECIPE

FERTILIZER REGIMEN

Amount of Water

Amount of Light

NOTES

Known Pests

Natural Habitat

Best Cultivation Environment

Why/How I haplessly MURDERED this plant:

SEASONAL OBSERVATIONS

Year One

SPRING

SUMMER

AUTUMN

WINTER

Year Two

SPRING

SUMMER

AUTUMN

WINTER

SKETCHES

NOTES

PLANT TAG

Light

Water

Spacing

Height

Soil Type

DETAIL 1

DETAIL 2

FAMILY	
GENUS	
SPECIES	

DATE OF ENTRY

ACQUIRED FROM

SEED GROWN	PURCHASED	CUTTING	FIELD COLLECTED
Date Sown	Supplier & Location		Date & Location: Did you do this sh*t ethically?

SOIL RECIPE

FERTILIZER REGIMEN

Amount of Water

Amount of Light

NOTES

Known Pests

Natural Habitat

Best Cultivation Environment

Why/How I haplessly MURDERED this plant:

SEASONAL OBSERVATIONS

Year One	SPRING	SUMMER	AUTUMN	WINTER
Year Two	SPRING	SUMMER	AUTUMN	WINTER

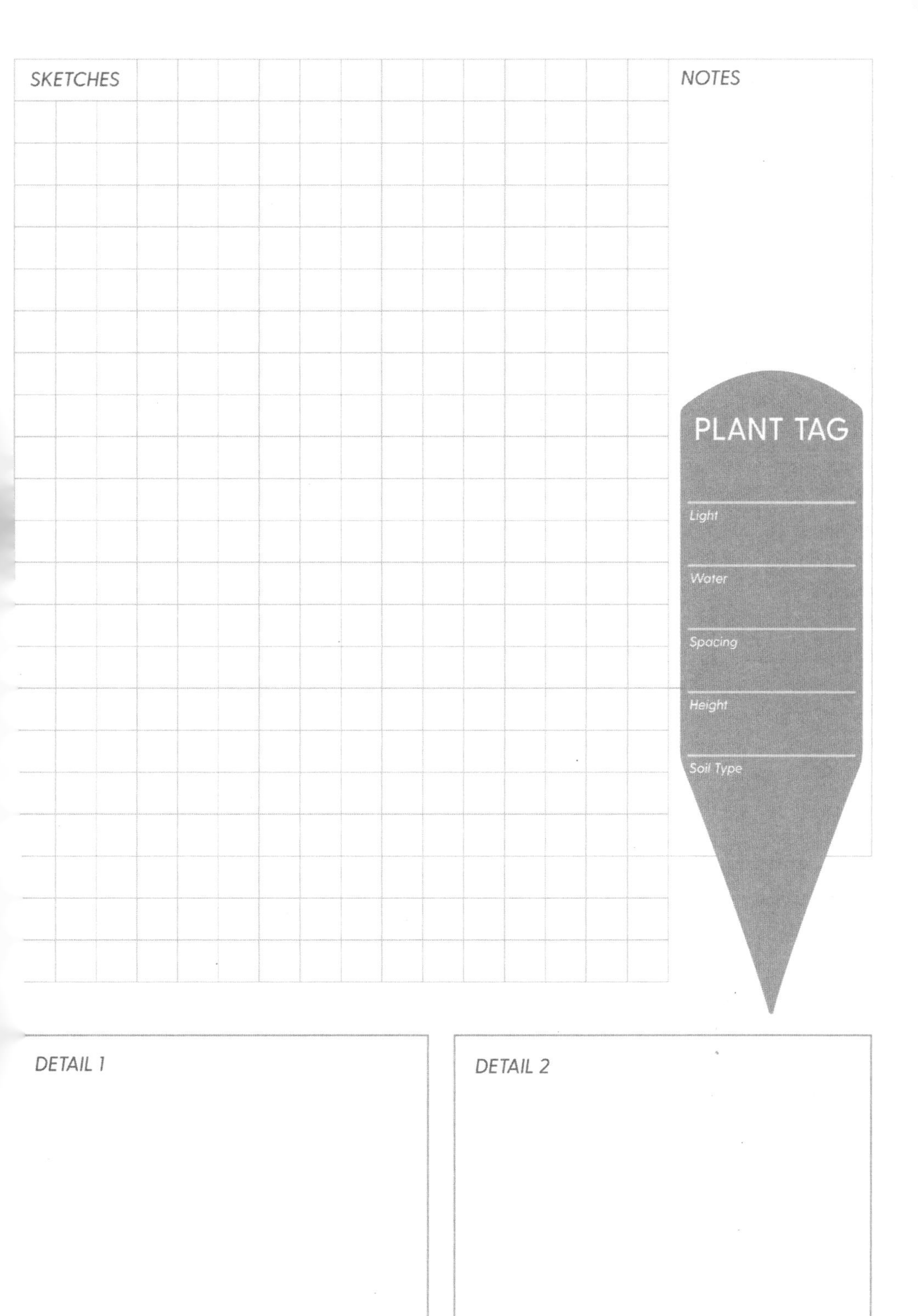

DETAIL 1

DETAIL 2

FAMILY
GENUS
SPECIES

DATE OF ENTRY

ACQUIRED FROM

SEED GROWN	PURCHASED	CUTTING	FIELD COLLECTED
Date Sown	Supplier & Location		Date & Location: Did you do this sh*t ethically?

SOIL RECIPE

FERTILIZER REGIMEN

Amount of Water

Amount of Light

NOTES

Known Pests

Natural Habitat

Best Cultivation Environment

Why/How I haplessly MURDERED this plant:

SEASONAL OBSERVATIONS

Year One

SPRING	SUMMER	AUTUMN	WINTER

Year Two

SPRING	SUMMER	AUTUMN	WINTER

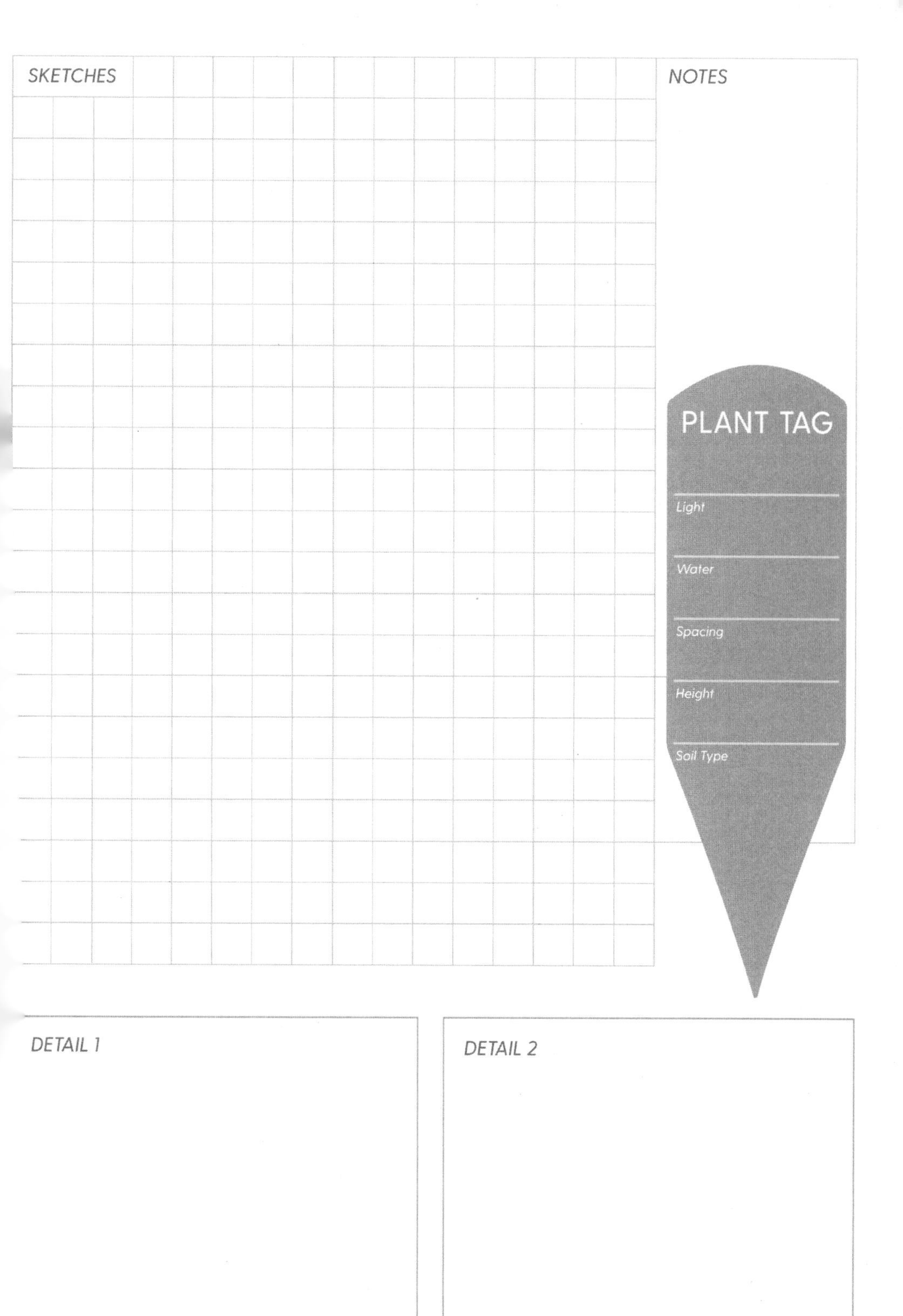

DETAIL 1

DETAIL 2

FAMILY

GENUS

SPECIES

DATE OF ENTRY

ACQUIRED FROM

SEED GROWN	PURCHASED	CUTTING	FIELD COLLECTED
Date Sown	Supplier & Location		Date & Location: Did you do this sh*t ethically?

SOIL RECIPE

FERTILIZER REGIMEN

Amount of Water

Amount of Light

NOTES

Known Pests

Natural Habitat

Best Cultivation Environment

Why/How I haplessly MURDERED this plant:

SEASONAL OBSERVATIONS

Year One	SPRING	SUMMER	AUTUMN	WINTER
Year Two	SPRING	SUMMER	AUTUMN	WINTER

SKETCHES

NOTES

PLANT TAG

Light

Water

Spacing

Height

Soil Type

DETAIL 1

DETAIL 2

FAMILY

GENUS

SPECIES

DATE OF ENTRY

ACQUIRED FROM

SEED GROWN	PURCHASED	CUTTING	FIELD COLLECTED
Date Sown	Supplier & Location		Date & Location: Did you do this sh*t ethically?

SOIL RECIPE

FERTILIZER REGIMEN

Amount of Water

Amount of Light

NOTES

Known Pests

Natural Habitat

Best Cultivation Environment

Why/How I haplessly MURDERED this plant:

SEASONAL OBSERVATIONS

Year One

SPRING	SUMMER	AUTUMN	WINTER

Year Two

SPRING	SUMMER	AUTUMN	WINTER

SKETCHES

NOTES

PLANT TAG

Light

Water

Spacing

Height

Soil Type

DETAIL 1

DETAIL 2

FAMILY

GENUS

SPECIES

DATE OF ENTRY

ACQUIRED FROM

SEED GROWN	PURCHASED	CUTTING	FIELD COLLECTED
Date Sown	Supplier & Location		Date & Location: Did you do this sh*t ethically?

SOIL RECIPE

FERTILIZER REGIMEN

Amount of Water

Amount of Light

NOTES

Known Pests

Natural Habitat

Best Cultivation Environment

Why/How I haplessly MURDERED this plant:

SEASONAL OBSERVATIONS

Year One

SPRING	SUMMER	AUTUMN	WINTER

Year Two

SPRING	SUMMER	AUTUMN	WINTER

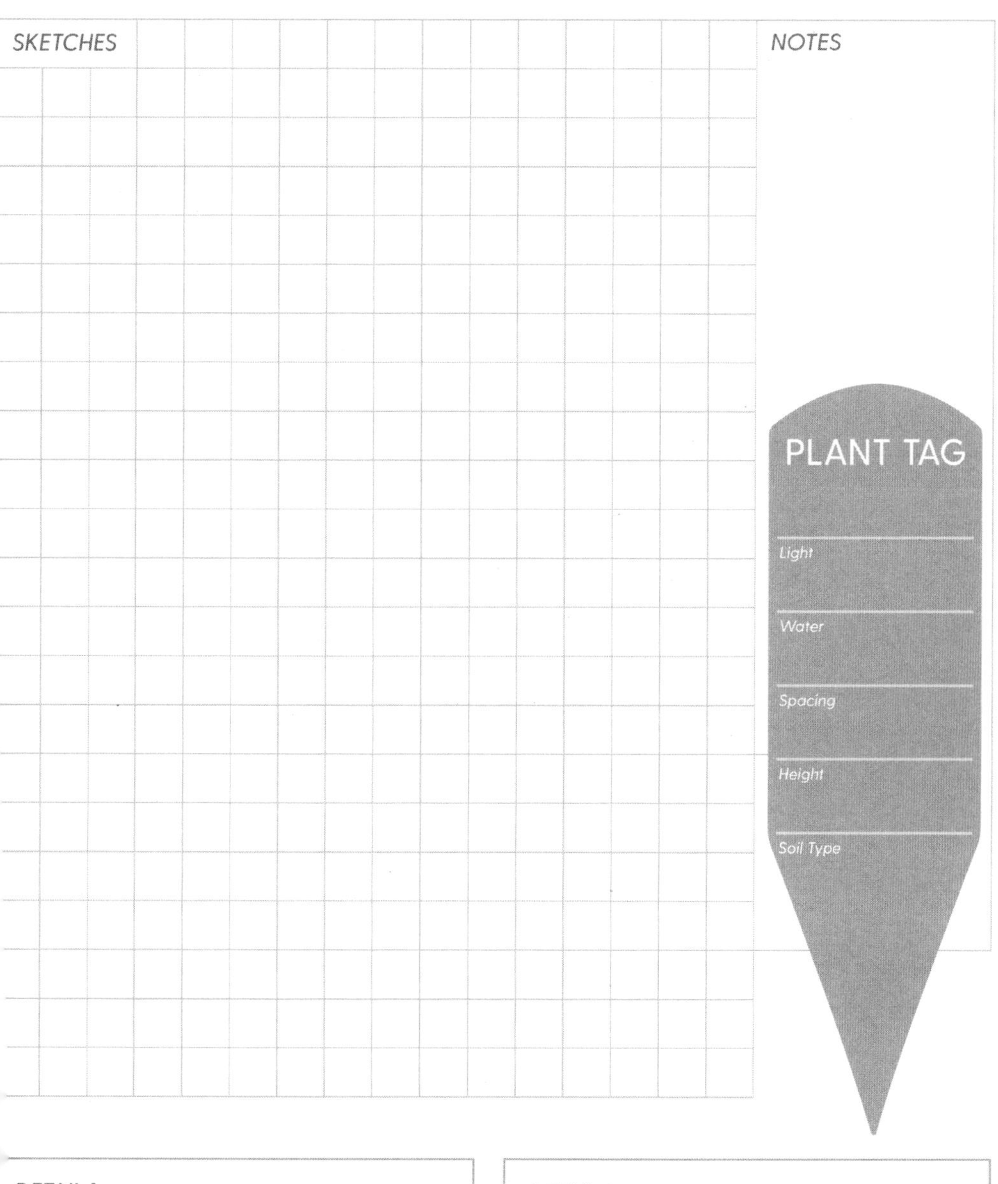

DETAIL 1

DETAIL 2

FAMILY

GENUS

SPECIES

DATE OF ENTRY

ACQUIRED FROM

SEED GROWN

Date Sown

PURCHASED

Supplier & Location

CUTTING

FIELD COLLECTED

Date & Location:

Did you do this sh*t ethically?

SOIL RECIPE

FERTILIZER REGIMEN

Amount of Water

Amount of Light

NOTES

Known Pests

Natural Habitat

Best Cultivation Environment

Why/How I haplessly MURDERED this plant:

SEASONAL OBSERVATIONS

Year One

SPRING	SUMMER	AUTUMN	WINTER

Year Two

SPRING	SUMMER	AUTUMN	WINTER

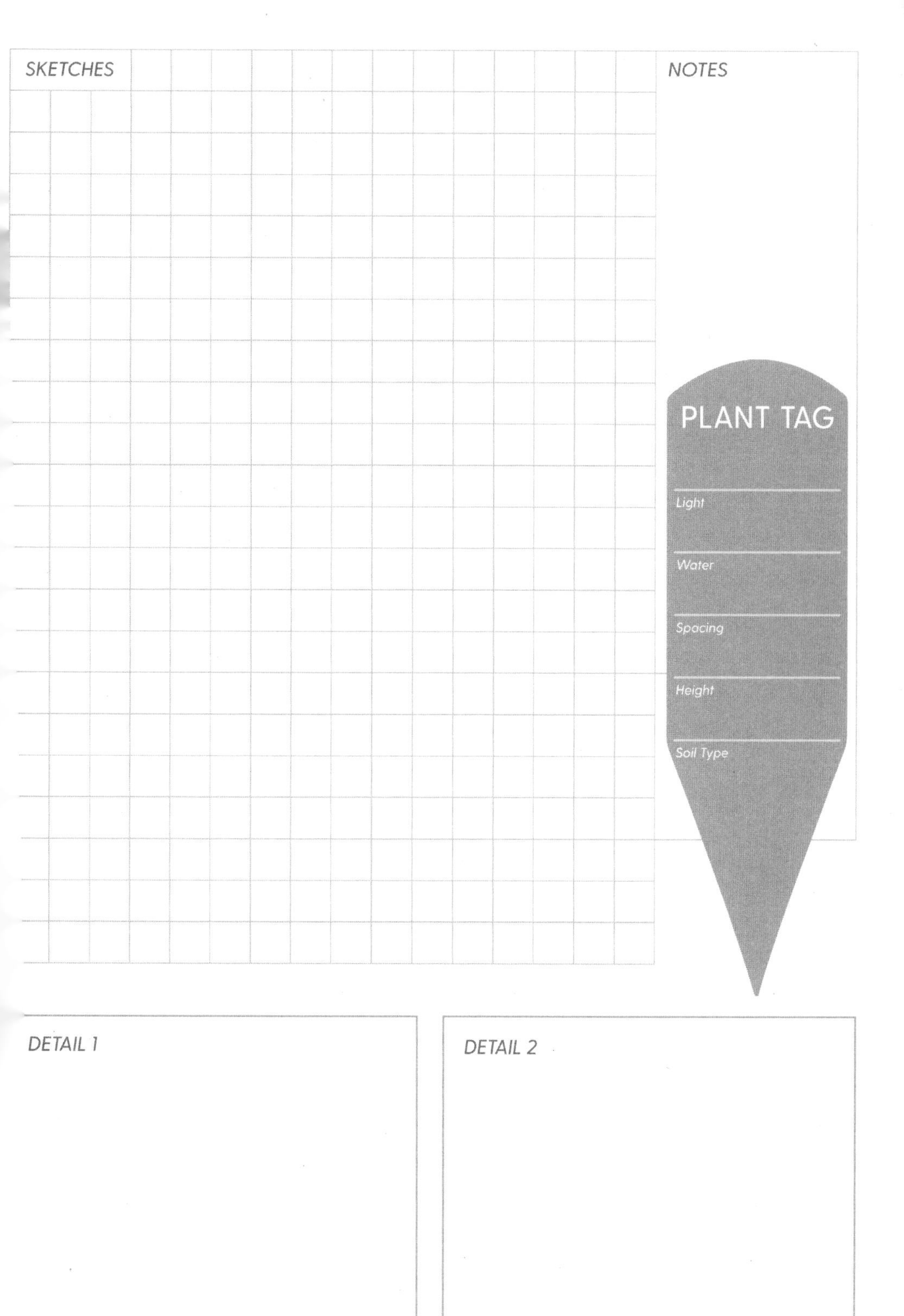

DETAIL 1

DETAIL 2

FAMILY

GENUS

SPECIES

DATE OF ENTRY

ACQUIRED FROM

SEED GROWN	PURCHASED	CUTTING	FIELD COLLECTED
Date Sown	Supplier & Location		Date & Location: Did you do this sh*t ethically?

SOIL RECIPE

FERTILIZER REGIMEN

Amount of Water

Amount of Light

NOTES

Known Pests

Natural Habitat

Best Cultivation Environment

Why/How I haplessly MURDERED this plant:

SEASONAL OBSERVATIONS

Year One

SPRING	SUMMER	AUTUMN	WINTER

Year Two

SPRING	SUMMER	AUTUMN	WINTER

SKETCHES

NOTES

PLANT TAG

Light

Water

Spacing

Height

Soil Type

DETAIL 1

DETAIL 2

FAMILY

GENUS

SPECIES

DATE OF ENTRY

ACQUIRED FROM

SEED GROWN	PURCHASED	CUTTING	FIELD COLLECTED
Date Sown	Supplier & Location		Date & Location: Did you do this sh*t ethically?

SOIL RECIPE

FERTILIZER REGIMEN

Amount of Water

Amount of Light

NOTES

Known Pests

Natural Habitat

Best Cultivation Environment

Why/How I haplessly MURDERED this plant:

SEASONAL OBSERVATIONS

	SPRING	SUMMER	AUTUMN	WINTER
Year One				
Year Two				

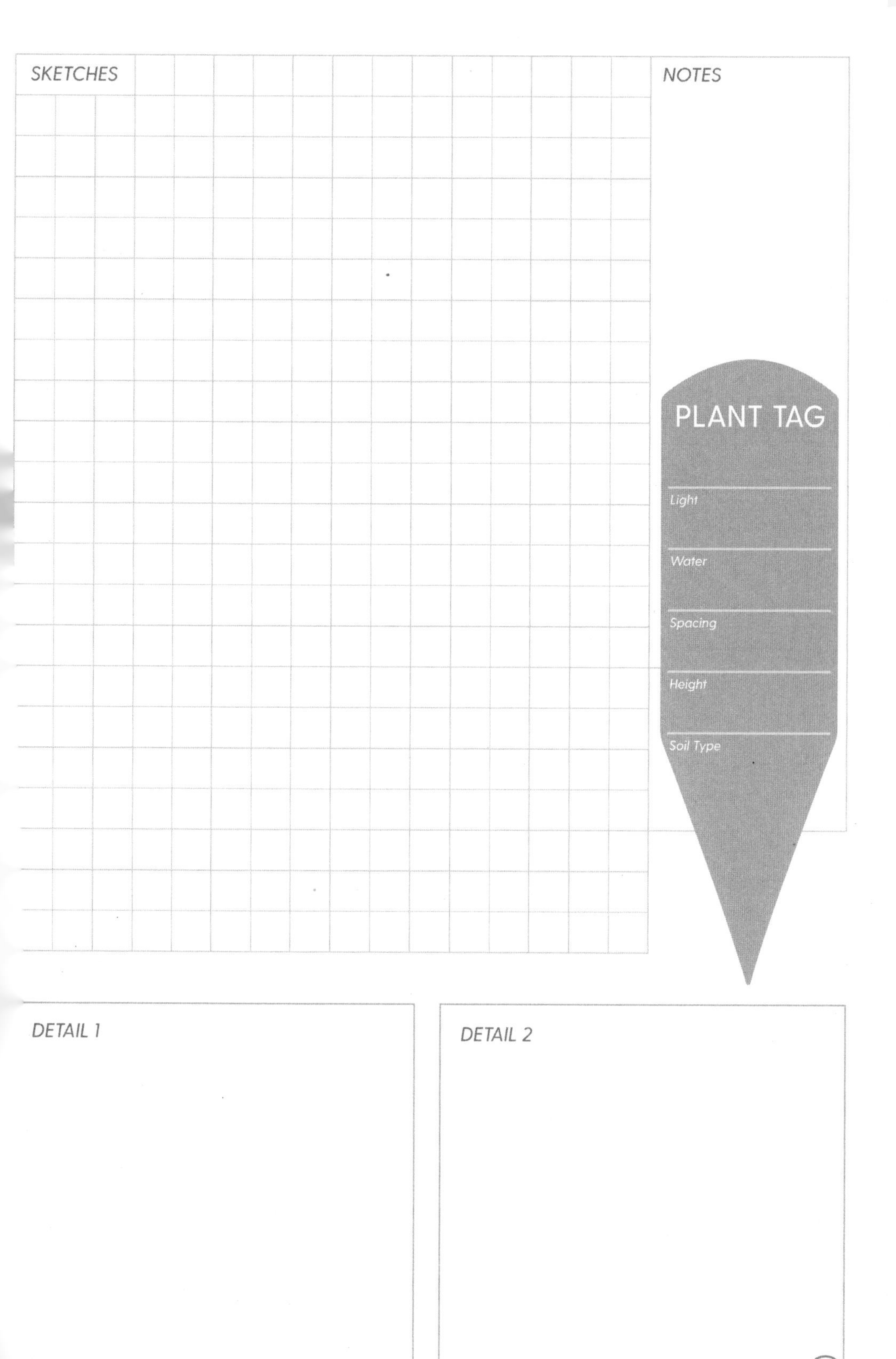

DETAIL 1

DETAIL 2

FAMILY	
GENUS	
SPECIES	

DATE OF ENTRY

ACQUIRED FROM

○ SEED GROWN	○ PURCHASED	○ CUTTING	○ FIELD COLLECTED
Date Sown	Supplier & Location		Date & Location: Did you do this sh*t ethically?

SOIL RECIPE

FERTILIZER REGIMEN

Amount of Water

Amount of Light

NOTES

Known Pests

Natural Habitat

Best Cultivation Environment

Why/How I haplessly MURDERED this plant:

SEASONAL OBSERVATIONS

Year One	SPRING	SUMMER	AUTUMN	WINTER
Year Two	SPRING	SUMMER	AUTUMN	WINTER

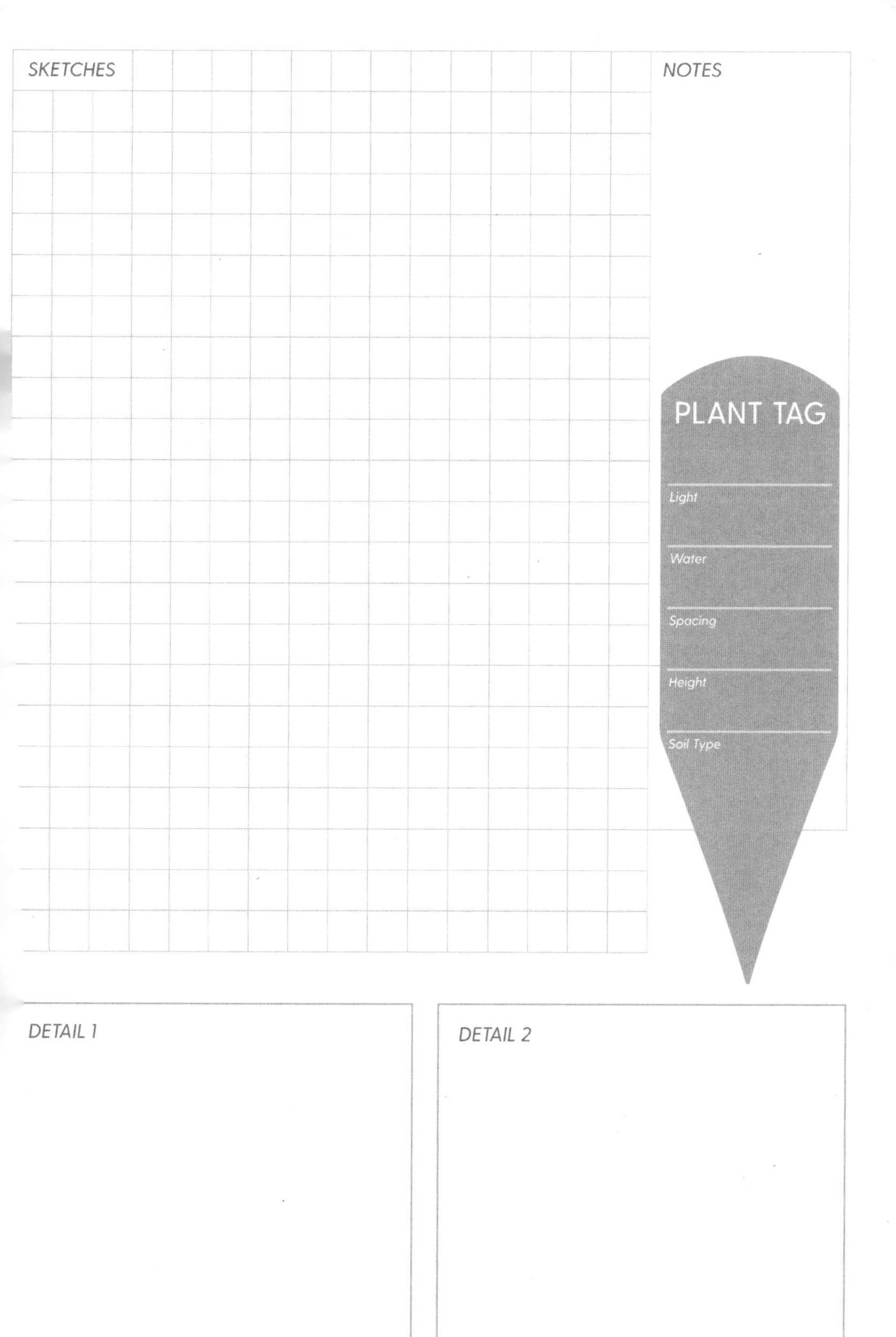
SKETCHES
NOTES
PLANT TAG
Light
Water
Spacing
Height
Soil Type
DETAIL 1
DETAIL 2

FAMILY

GENUS

SPECIES

DATE OF ENTRY

ACQUIRED FROM

SEED GROWN	PURCHASED	CUTTING	FIELD COLLECTED
Date Sown	Supplier & Location		Date & Location: Did you do this sh*t ethically?

SOIL RECIPE

FERTILIZER REGIMEN

Amount of Water

Amount of Light

NOTES

Known Pests

Natural Habitat

Best Cultivation Environment

Why/How I haplessly MURDERED this plant:

SEASONAL OBSERVATIONS

Year One

SPRING	SUMMER	AUTUMN	WINTER

Year Two

SPRING	SUMMER	AUTUMN	WINTER

Garden Planner

This page is meant to serve as your personal garden brainstorming companion. Whether you need you a blank canvas to dump your gardening ideas or strategically lay out your landscaping dreams, a garden planner is your collaborator.

A cardinal rose is included to help indicate the direction your plants and garden will face as lighting is arguably the most vital element when it comes to being a successful grower. Sit outside and take notes on lighting, intensity and even moments of shade throughout the day and seasons.

In the Garden Key at right, mark your plants with little icons or doodles to indicate where things lie in your plot. Don't worry about being the next Bernini when scribbling out the angles of your blackberry leaves, that's crazy and uneccesary. Think of this as a visual notebook, but filled with things you hope to not kill.

While this page exists with the outdoor gardener in mind, there's no reason you can't make use of it while arranging your greenhouse or finding the most ideal locations for your house plants!

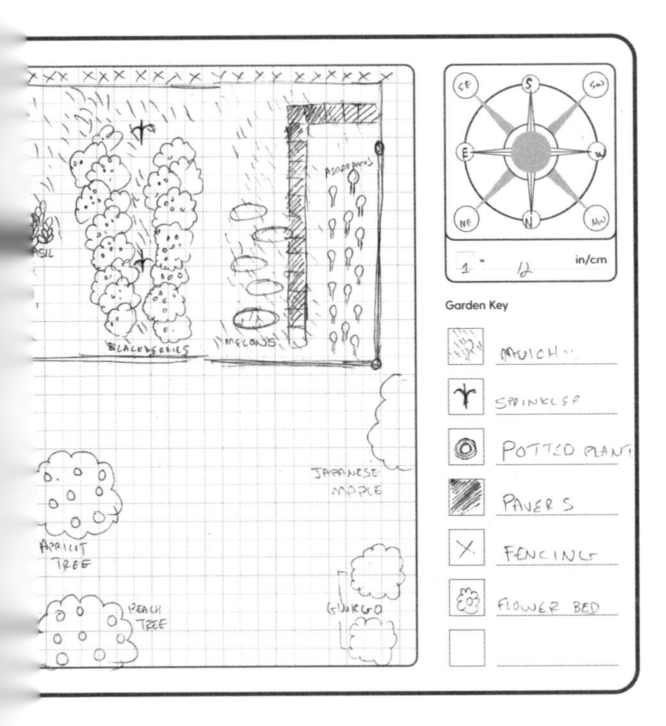

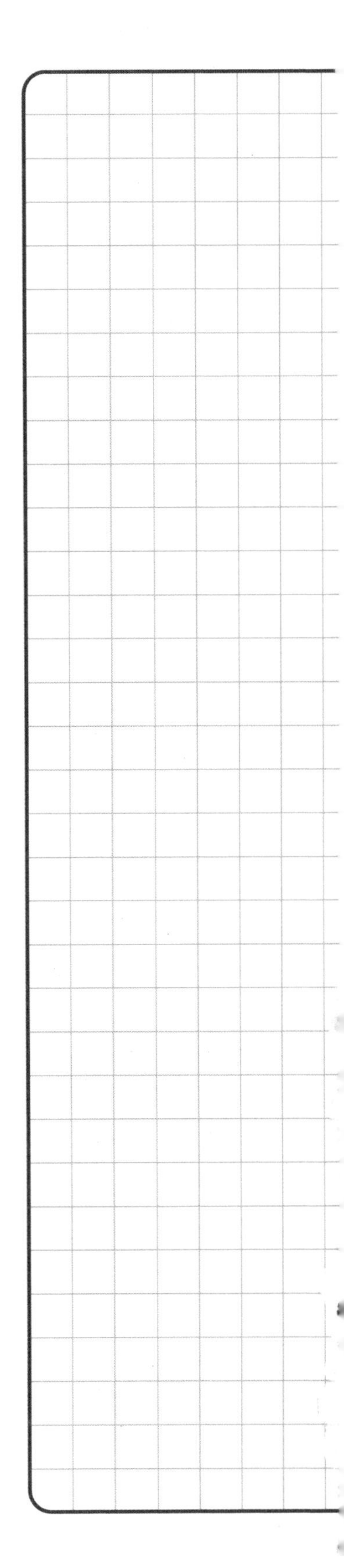

FAMILY

GENUS

SPECIES

DATE OF ENTRY

ACQUIRED FROM

SEED GROWN

Date Sown

PURCHASED

Supplier & Location

CUTTING

FIELD COLLECTED

Date & Location:

Did you do this sh*t ethically?

SOIL RECIPE

FERTILIZER REGIMEN

Amount of Water

Amount of Light

NOTES

Known Pests

Natural Habitat

Best Cultivation Environment

Why/How I haplessly MURDERED this plant:

SEASONAL OBSERVATIONS

Year One

SPRING

SUMMER

AUTUMN

WINTER

Year Two

SPRING

SUMMER

AUTUMN

WINTER

SKETCHES

NOTES

PLANT TAG

Light

Water

Spacing

Height

Soil Type

DETAIL 1

DETAIL 2

FAMILY

GENUS

SPECIES

DATE OF ENTRY

ACQUIRED FROM

SEED GROWN	PURCHASED	CUTTING	FIELD COLLECTED
Date Sown	Supplier & Location		Date & Location: Did you do this sh*t ethically?

SOIL RECIPE

FERTILIZER REGIMEN

Amount of Water

Amount of Light

NOTES

Known Pests

Natural Habitat

Best Cultivation Environment

Why/How I haplessly MURDERED this plant:

SEASONAL OBSERVATIONS

Year One

SPRING	SUMMER	AUTUMN	WINTER

Year Two

SPRING	SUMMER	AUTUMN	WINTER

SKETCHES

NOTES

PLANT TAG

Light

Water

Spacing

Height

Soil Type

DETAIL 1

DETAIL 2

FAMILY

GENUS

SPECIES

DATE OF ENTRY

ACQUIRED FROM

SEED GROWN	PURCHASED	CUTTING	FIELD COLLECTED
Date Sown	Supplier & Location		Date & Location: Did you do this sh*t ethically?

SOIL RECIPE

FERTILIZER REGIMEN

Amount of Water

Amount of Light

NOTES

Known Pests

Natural Habitat

Best Cultivation Environment

Why/How I haplessly MURDERED this plant:

SEASONAL OBSERVATIONS

Year One

SPRING	SUMMER	AUTUMN	WINTER

Year Two

SPRING	SUMMER	AUTUMN	WINTER

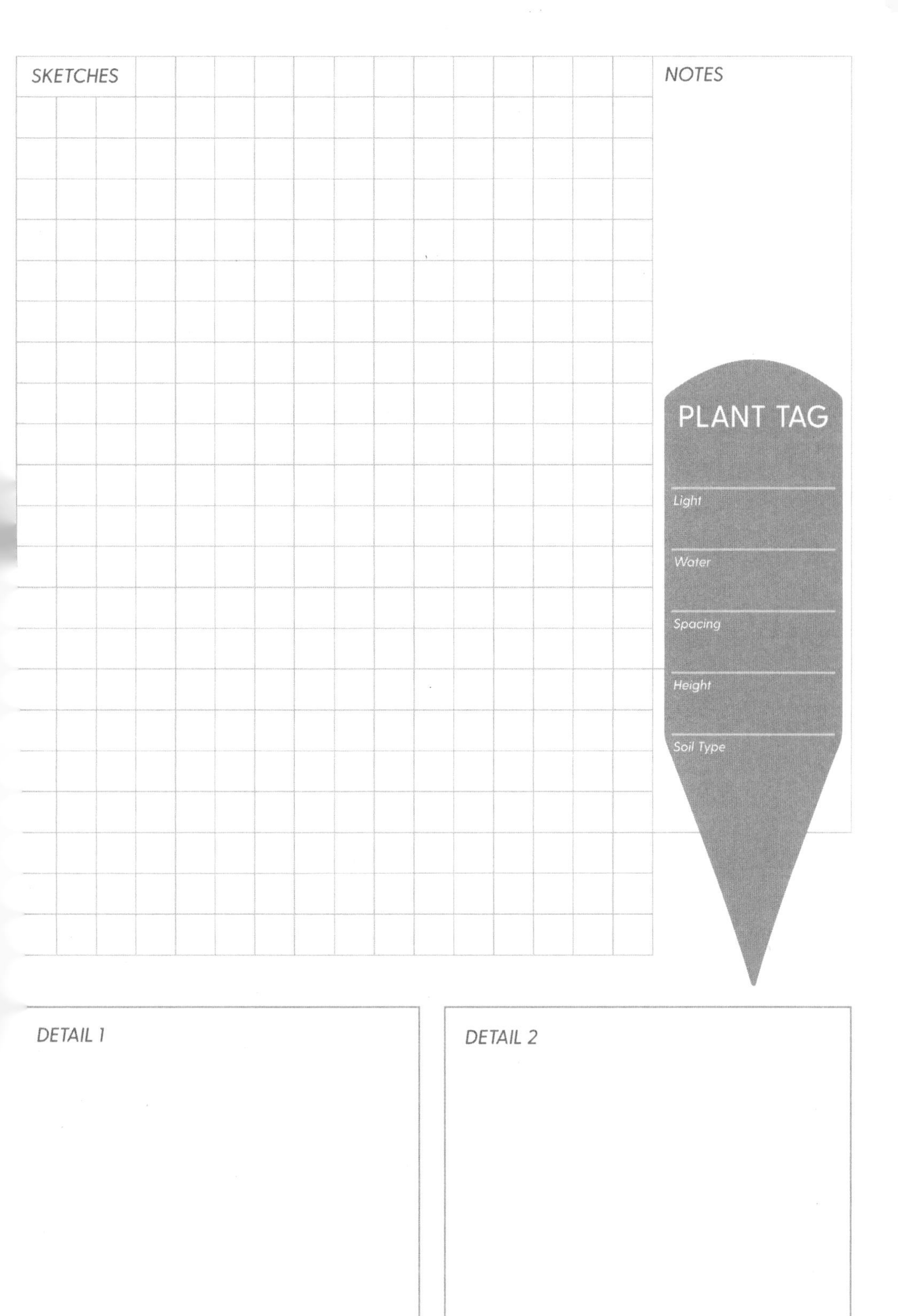
SKETCHES
NOTES
PLANT TAG
Light
Water
Spacing
Height
Soil Type
DETAIL 1
DETAIL 2

FAMILY

GENUS

SPECIES

DATE OF ENTRY

ACQUIRED FROM

SEED GROWN	PURCHASED	CUTTING	FIELD COLLECTED
Date Sown	Supplier & Location		Date & Location: Did you do this sh*t ethically?

SOIL RECIPE

FERTILIZER REGIMEN

Amount of Water

Amount of Light

NOTES

Known Pests

Natural Habitat

Best Cultivation Environment

Why/How I haplessly MURDERED this plant:

SEASONAL OBSERVATIONS

Year One

SPRING	SUMMER	AUTUMN	WINTER

Year Two

SPRING	SUMMER	AUTUMN	WINTER

SKETCHES

NOTES

PLANT TAG

Light

Water

Spacing

Height

Soil Type

DETAIL 1

DETAIL 2

FAMILY

GENUS

SPECIES

DATE OF ENTRY

ACQUIRED FROM

SEED GROWN

Date Sown

PURCHASED

Supplier & Location

CUTTING

FIELD COLLECTED

Date & Location:

Did you do this sh*t ethically?

SOIL RECIPE

FERTILIZER REGIMEN

Amount of Water

Amount of Light

NOTES

Known Pests

Natural Habitat

Best Cultivation Environment

Why/How I haplessly MURDERED this plant:

SEASONAL OBSERVATIONS

Year One

SPRING	SUMMER	AUTUMN	WINTER

Year Two

SPRING	SUMMER	AUTUMN	WINTER

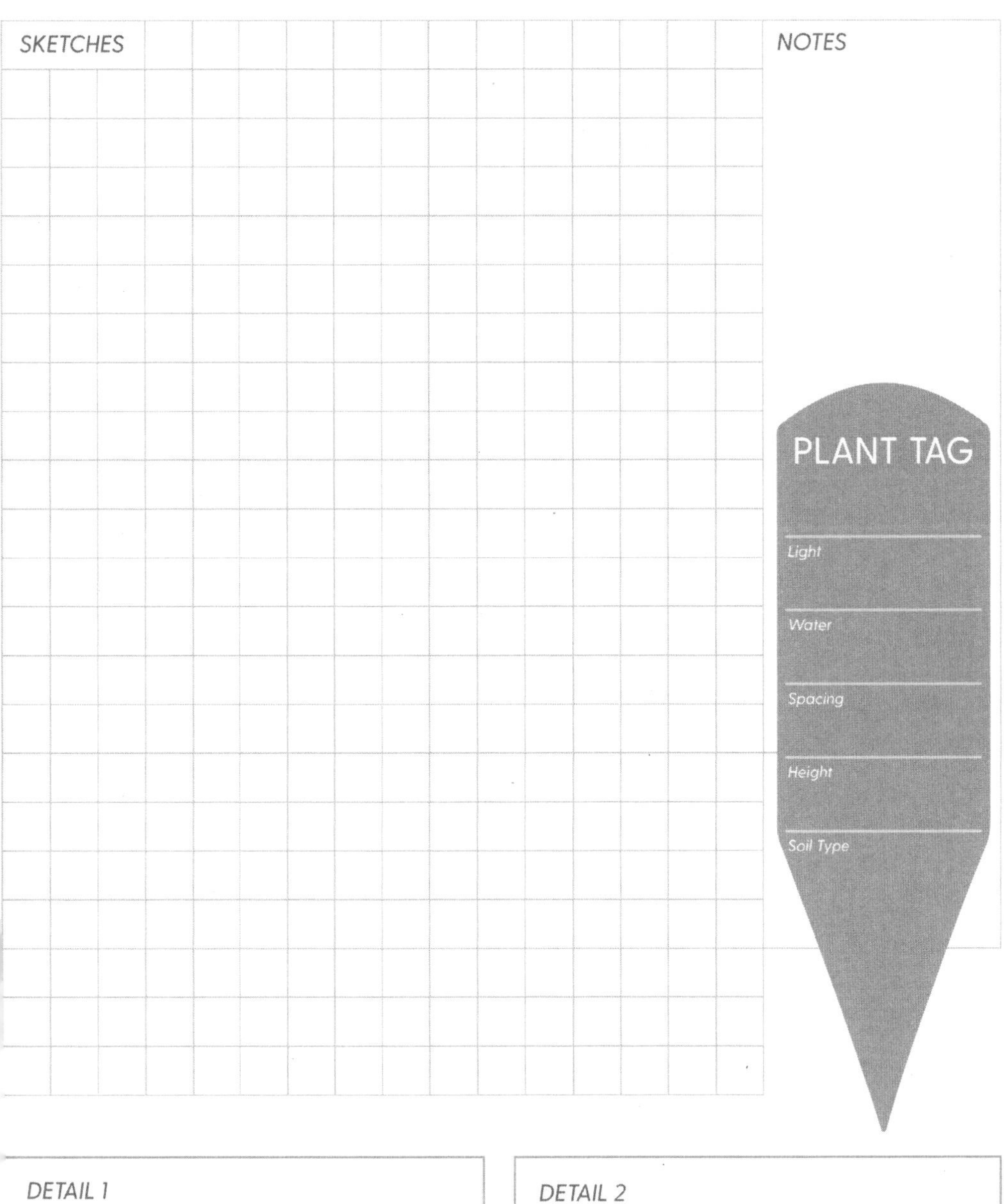

DETAIL 1

DETAIL 2

FAMILY

GENUS

SPECIES

DATE OF ENTRY

ACQUIRED FROM

SEED GROWN	PURCHASED	CUTTING	FIELD COLLECTED
Date Sown	Supplier & Location		Date & Location: Did you do this sh*t ethically?

SOIL RECIPE

FERTILIZER REGIMEN

Amount of Water

Amount of Light

NOTES

Known Pests

Natural Habitat

Best Cultivation Environment

Why/How I haplessly MURDERED this plant:

SEASONAL OBSERVATIONS

Year One

SPRING	SUMMER	AUTUMN	WINTER

Year Two

SPRING	SUMMER	AUTUMN	WINTER

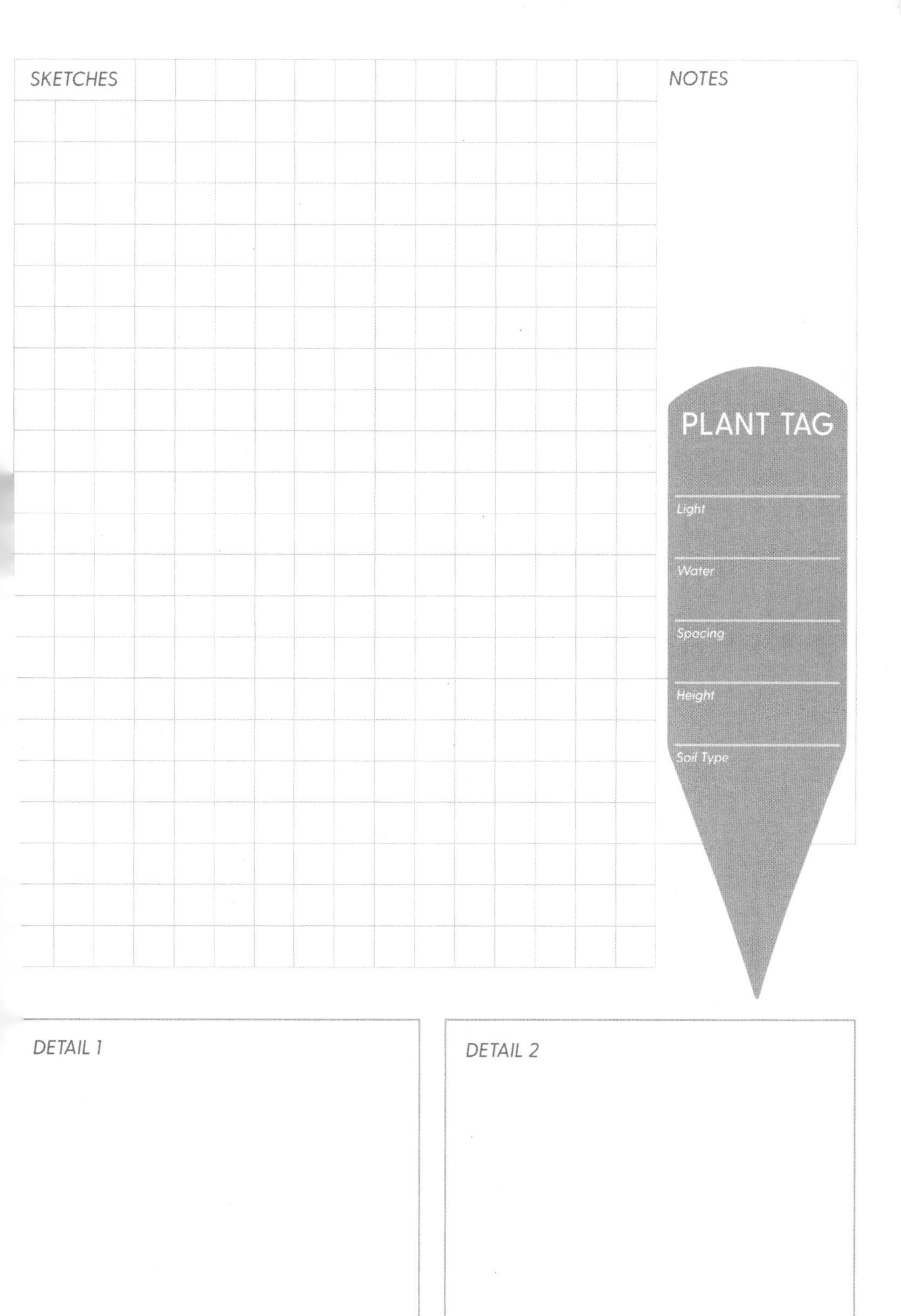

DETAIL 1

DETAIL 2

FAMILY

GENUS

SPECIES

DATE OF ENTRY

ACQUIRED FROM

SEED GROWN	PURCHASED	CUTTING	FIELD COLLECTED
Date Sown	Supplier & Location		Date & Location: Did you do this sh*t ethically?

SOIL RECIPE

FERTILIZER REGIMEN

Amount of Water

Amount of Light

NOTES

Known Pests

Natural Habitat

Best Cultivation Environment

Why/How I haplessly MURDERED this plant:

SEASONAL OBSERVATIONS

Year One

SPRING	SUMMER	AUTUMN	WINTER

Year Two

SPRING	SUMMER	AUTUMN	WINTER

SKETCHES

NOTES

PLANT TAG

Light

Water

Spacing

Height

Soil Type

DETAIL 1

DETAIL 2

FAMILY

GENUS

SPECIES

DATE OF ENTRY

ACQUIRED FROM

SEED GROWN	PURCHASED	CUTTING	FIELD COLLECTED
Date Sown	Supplier & Location		Date & Location: Did you do this sh*t ethically?

SOIL RECIPE

FERTILIZER REGIMEN

Amount of Water

Amount of Light

NOTES

Known Pests

Natural Habitat

Best Cultivation Environment

Why/How I haplessly MURDERED this plant:

SEASONAL OBSERVATIONS

Year One

SPRING	SUMMER	AUTUMN	WINTER

Year Two

SPRING	SUMMER	AUTUMN	WINTER

SKETCHES

NOTES

PLANT TAG

Light

Water

Spacing

Height

Soil Type

DETAIL 1

DETAIL 2

FAMILY

GENUS

SPECIES

DATE OF ENTRY

ACQUIRED FROM

SEED GROWN	PURCHASED	CUTTING	FIELD COLLECTED
Date Sown	Supplier & Location		Date & Location: Did you do this sh*t ethically?

SOIL RECIPE

FERTILIZER REGIMEN

Amount of Water

Amount of Light

NOTES

Known Pests

Natural Habitat

Best Cultivation Environment

Why/How I haplessly MÜRDERED this plant:

SEASONAL OBSERVATIONS

Year One

SPRING	SUMMER	AUTUMN	WINTER

Year Two

SPRING	SUMMER	AUTUMN	WINTER

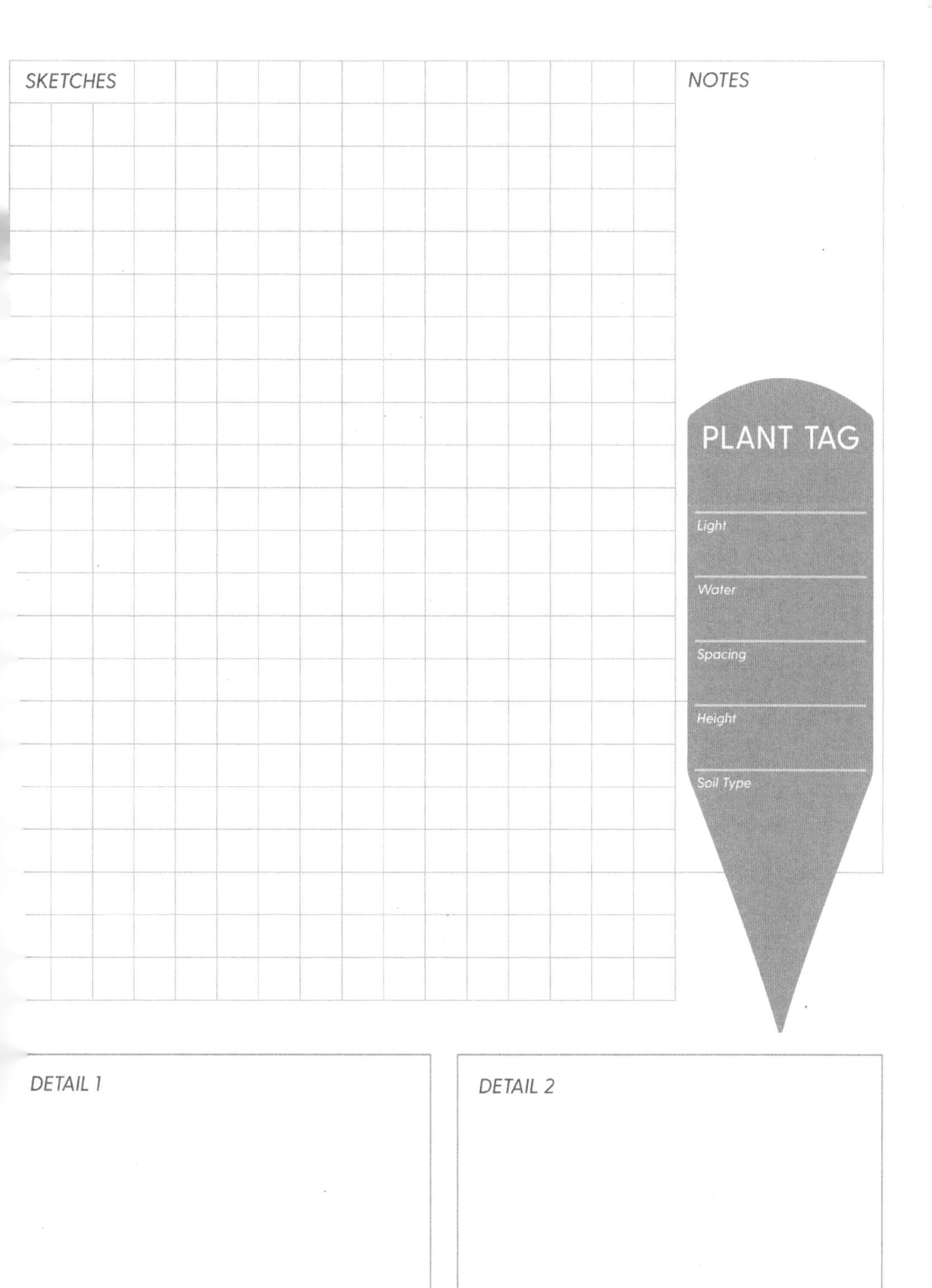

DETAIL 1

DETAIL 2

FAMILY

GENUS

SPECIES

DATE OF ENTRY

ACQUIRED FROM

SEED GROWN

Date Sown

PURCHASED

Supplier & Location

CUTTING

FIELD COLLECTED

Date & Location:

Did you do this sh*t ethically?

SOIL RECIPE

FERTILIZER REGIMEN

Amount of Water

Amount of Light

NOTES

Known Pests

Natural Habitat

Best Cultivation Environment

Why/How I haplessly MURDERED this plant:

SEASONAL OBSERVATIONS

Year One

SPRING	SUMMER	AUTUMN	WINTER

Year Two

SPRING	SUMMER	AUTUMN	WINTER

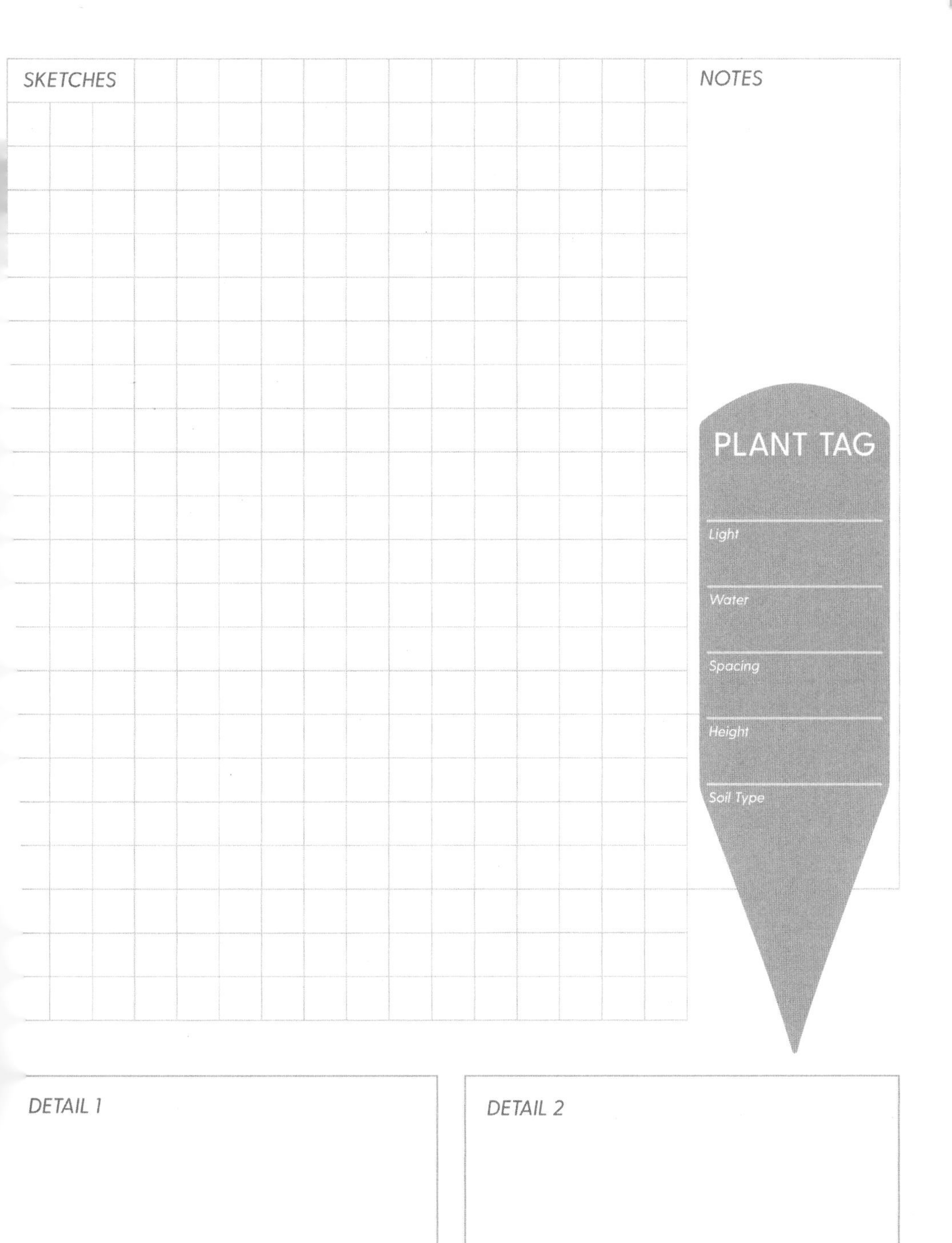

DETAIL 1

DETAIL 2

FAMILY	
GENUS	
SPECIES	

DATE OF ENTRY

ACQUIRED FROM

SEED GROWN	PURCHASED	CUTTING	FIELD COLLECTED
Date Sown	Supplier & Location		Date & Location: Did you do this sh*t ethically?

SOIL RECIPE

FERTILIZER REGIMEN

Amount of Water

Amount of Light

NOTES

Known Pests

Natural Habitat

Best Cultivation Environment

Why/How I haplessly MURDERED this plant:

SEASONAL OBSERVATIONS

Year One

SPRING	SUMMER	AUTUMN	WINTER

Year Two

SPRING	SUMMER	AUTUMN	WINTER

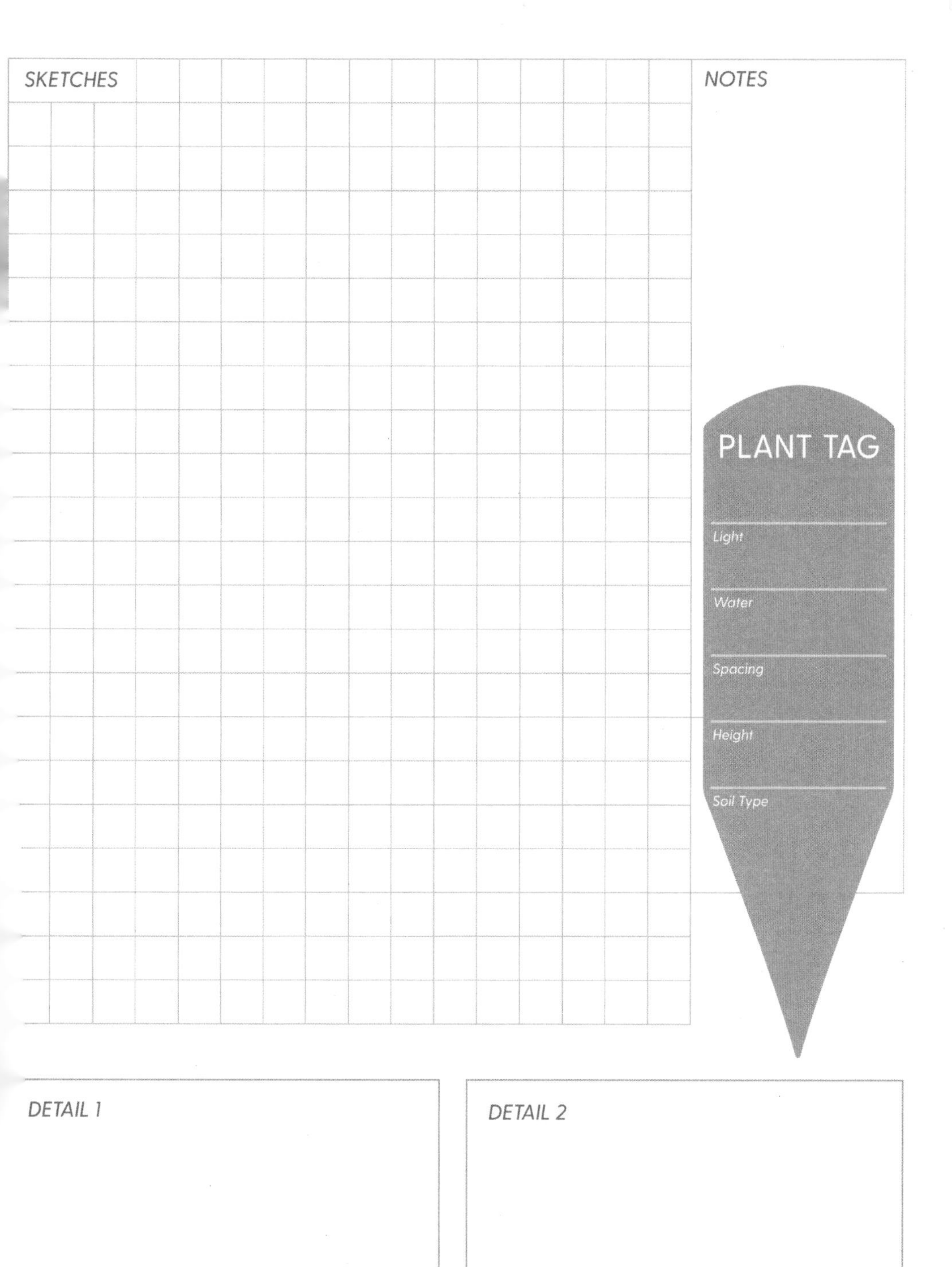

DETAIL 1

DETAIL 2

FAMILY

GENUS

SPECIES

DATE OF ENTRY

ACQUIRED FROM

SEED GROWN	PURCHASED	CUTTING	FIELD COLLECTED
Date Sown	Supplier & Location		Date & Location: Did you do this sh*t ethically?

SOIL RECIPE

FERTILIZER REGIMEN

Amount of Water

Amount of Light

NOTES

Known Pests

Natural Habitat

Best Cultivation Environment

Why/How I haplessly MURDERED this plant:

SEASONAL OBSERVATIONS

Year One

SPRING	SUMMER	AUTUMN	WINTER

Year Two

SPRING	SUMMER	AUTUMN	WINTER

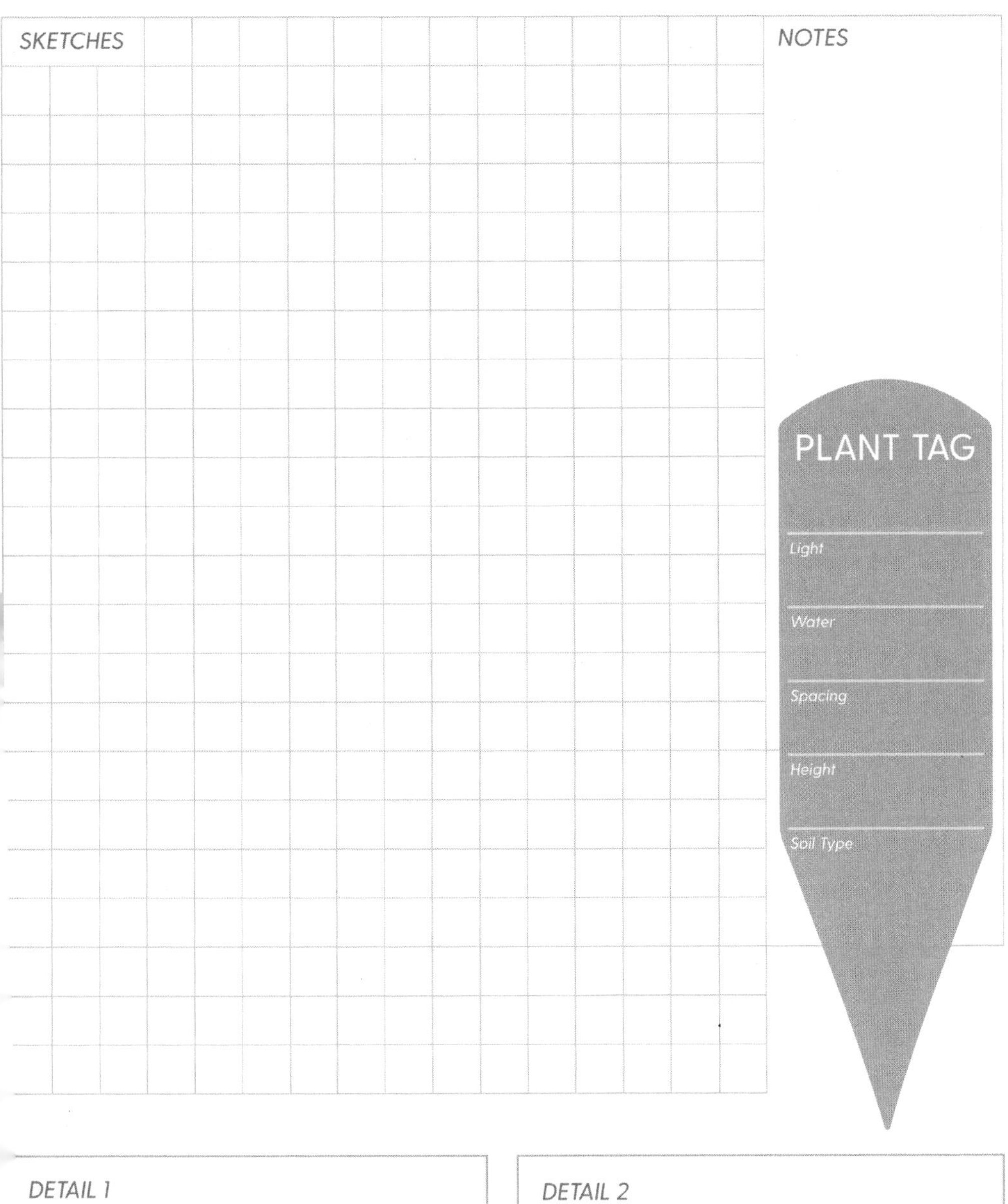

DETAIL 1

DETAIL 2

FAMILY

GENUS

SPECIES

DATE OF ENTRY

ACQUIRED FROM

SEED GROWN	PURCHASED	CUTTING	FIELD COLLECTED
Date Sown	Supplier & Location		Date & Location: Did you do this sh*t ethically?

SOIL RECIPE

FERTILIZER REGIMEN

Amount of Water

Amount of Light

NOTES

Known Pests

Natural Habitat

Best Cultivation Environment

Why/How I haplessly MURDERED this plant:

SEASONAL OBSERVATIONS

Year One

SPRING	SUMMER	AUTUMN	WINTER

Year Two

SPRING	SUMMER	AUTUMN	WINTER

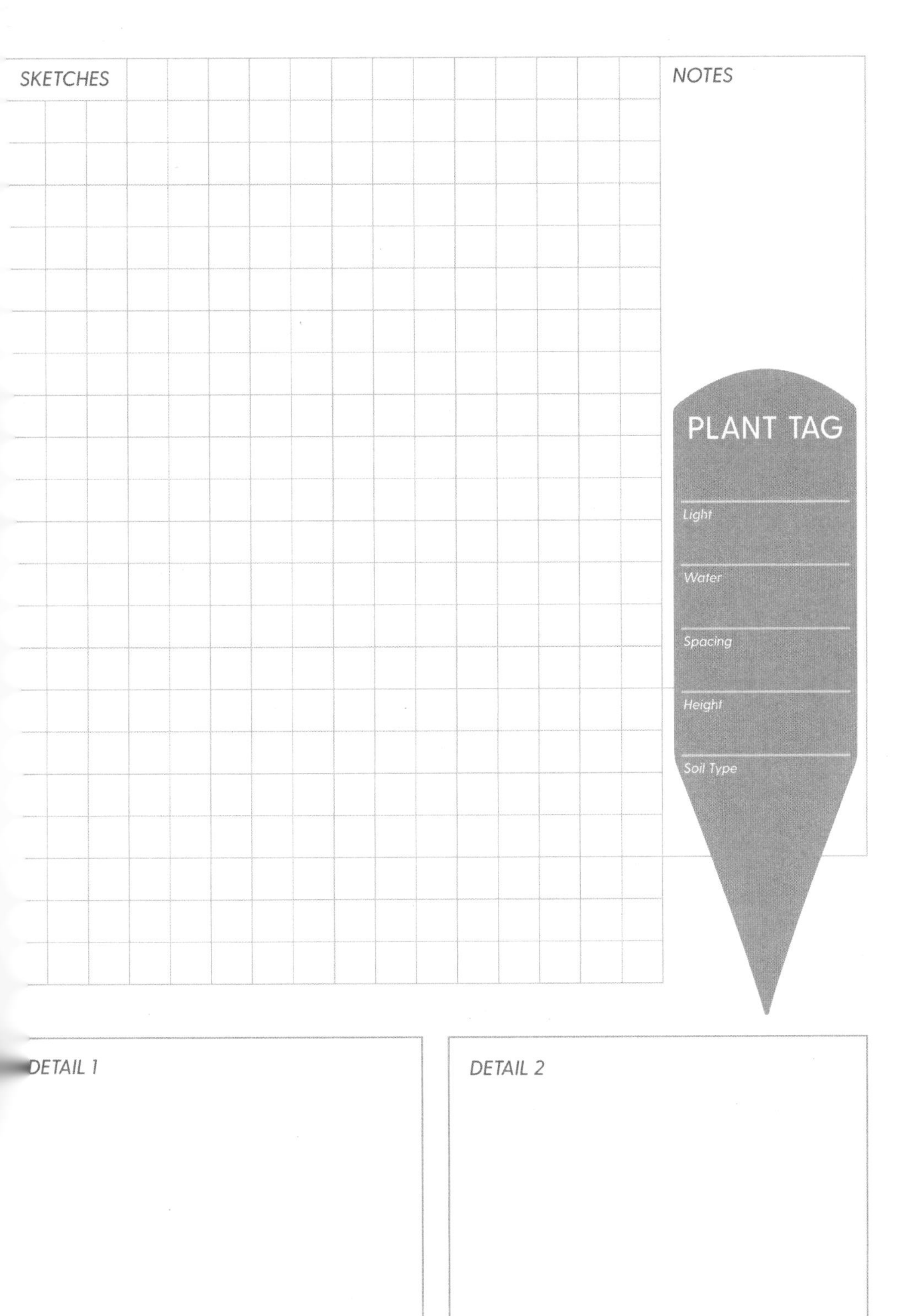
SKETCHES
NOTES
PLANT TAG
Light
Water
Spacing
Height
Soil Type
DETAIL 1
DETAIL 2

FAMILY

GENUS

SPECIES

DATE OF ENTRY

ACQUIRED FROM

SEED GROWN	PURCHASED	CUTTING	FIELD COLLECTED
Date Sown	Supplier & Location		Date & Location: Did you do this sh*t ethically?

SOIL RECIPE

FERTILIZER REGIMEN

Amount of Water

Amount of Light

NOTES

Known Pests

Natural Habitat

Best Cultivation Environment

Why/How I haplessly MURDERED this plant:

SEASONAL OBSERVATIONS

Year One

SPRING	SUMMER	AUTUMN.	WINTER

Year Two

SPRING	SUMMER	AUTUMN	WINTER

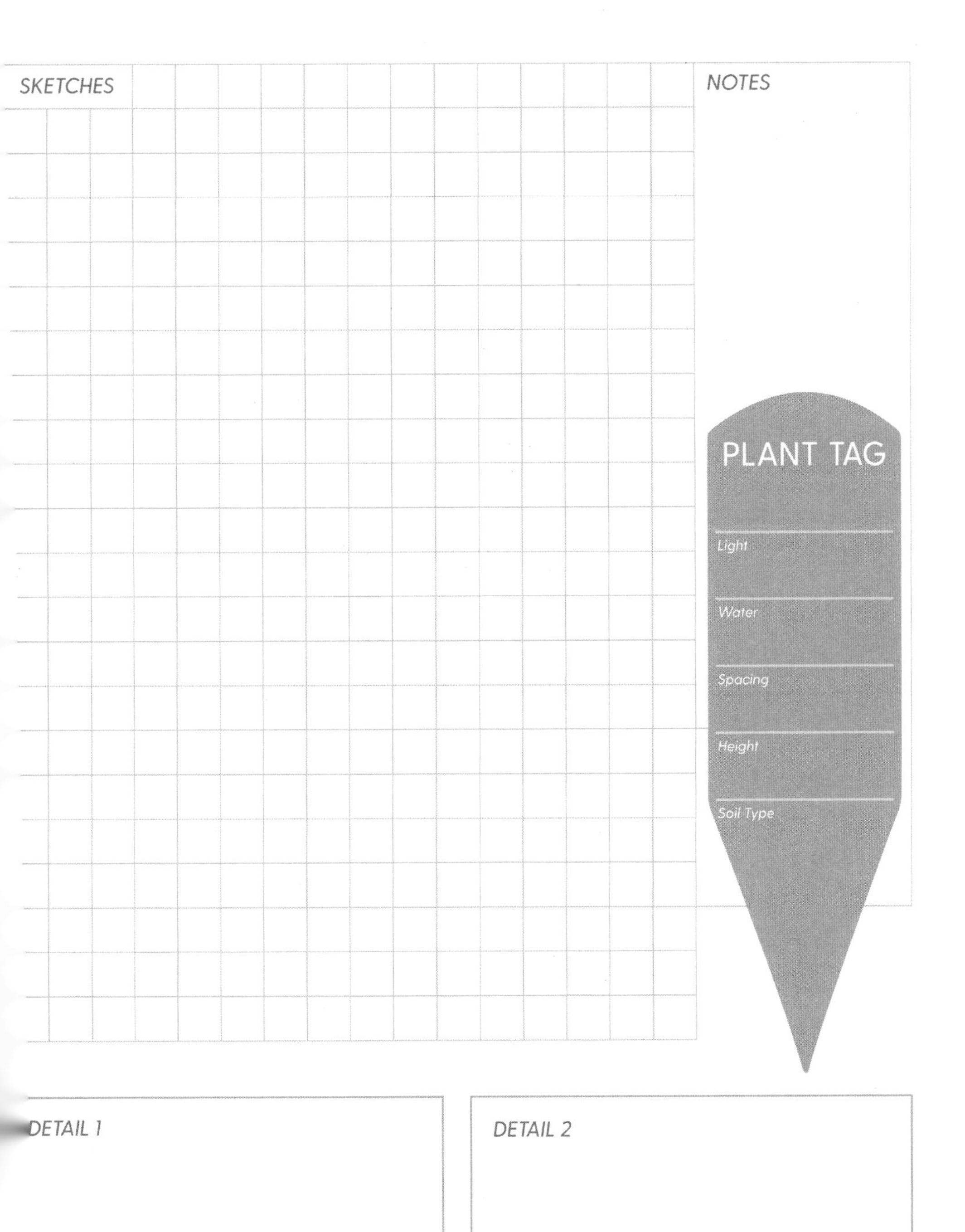

DETAIL 1

DETAIL 2

FAMILY

GENUS

SPECIES

DATE OF ENTRY

ACQUIRED FROM

SEED GROWN	PURCHASED	CUTTING	FIELD COLLECTED
Date Sown	Supplier & Location		Date & Location: Did you do this sh*t ethically?

SOIL RECIPE

FERTILIZER REGIMEN

Amount of Water

Amount of Light

NOTES

Known Pests

Natural Habitat

Best Cultivation Environment

Why/How I haplessly MURDERED this plant:

SEASONAL OBSERVATIONS

Year One

SPRING	SUMMER	AUTUMN	WINTER

Year Two

SPRING	SUMMER	AUTUMN	WINTER

SKETCHES

NOTES

PLANT TAG

Light

Water

Spacing

Height

Soil Type

DETAIL 1

DETAIL 2

FAMILY

GENUS

SPECIES

DATE OF ENTRY

ACQUIRED FROM

SEED GROWN	PURCHASED	CUTTING	FIELD COLLECTED
Date Sown	Supplier & Location		Date & Location: Did you do this sh*t ethically?

SOIL RECIPE

FERTILIZER REGIMEN

Amount of Water

Amount of Light

NOTES

Known Pests

Natural Habitat

Best Cultivation Environment

Why/How I haplessly MURDERED this plant:

SEASONAL OBSERVATIONS

Year One

SPRING	SUMMER	AUTUMN	WINTER

Year Two

SPRING	SUMMER	AUTUMN	WINTER

SKETCHES

NOTES

PLANT TAG

Light

Water

Spacing

Height

Soil Type

DETAIL 1

DETAIL 2

FAMILY	
GENUS	
SPECIES	

DATE OF ENTRY

ACQUIRED FROM

SEED GROWN	PURCHASED	CUTTING	FIELD COLLECTED
Date Sown	Supplier & Location		Date & Location: Did you do this sh*t ethically?

SOIL RECIPE

FERTILIZER REGIMEN

Amount of Water

Amount of Light

NOTES

Known Pests

Natural Habitat

Best Cultivation Environment

Why/How I haplessly MURDERED this plant:

SEASONAL OBSERVATIONS

Year One	SPRING	SUMMER	AUTUMN	WINTER
Year Two	SPRING	SUMMER	AUTUMN	WINTER

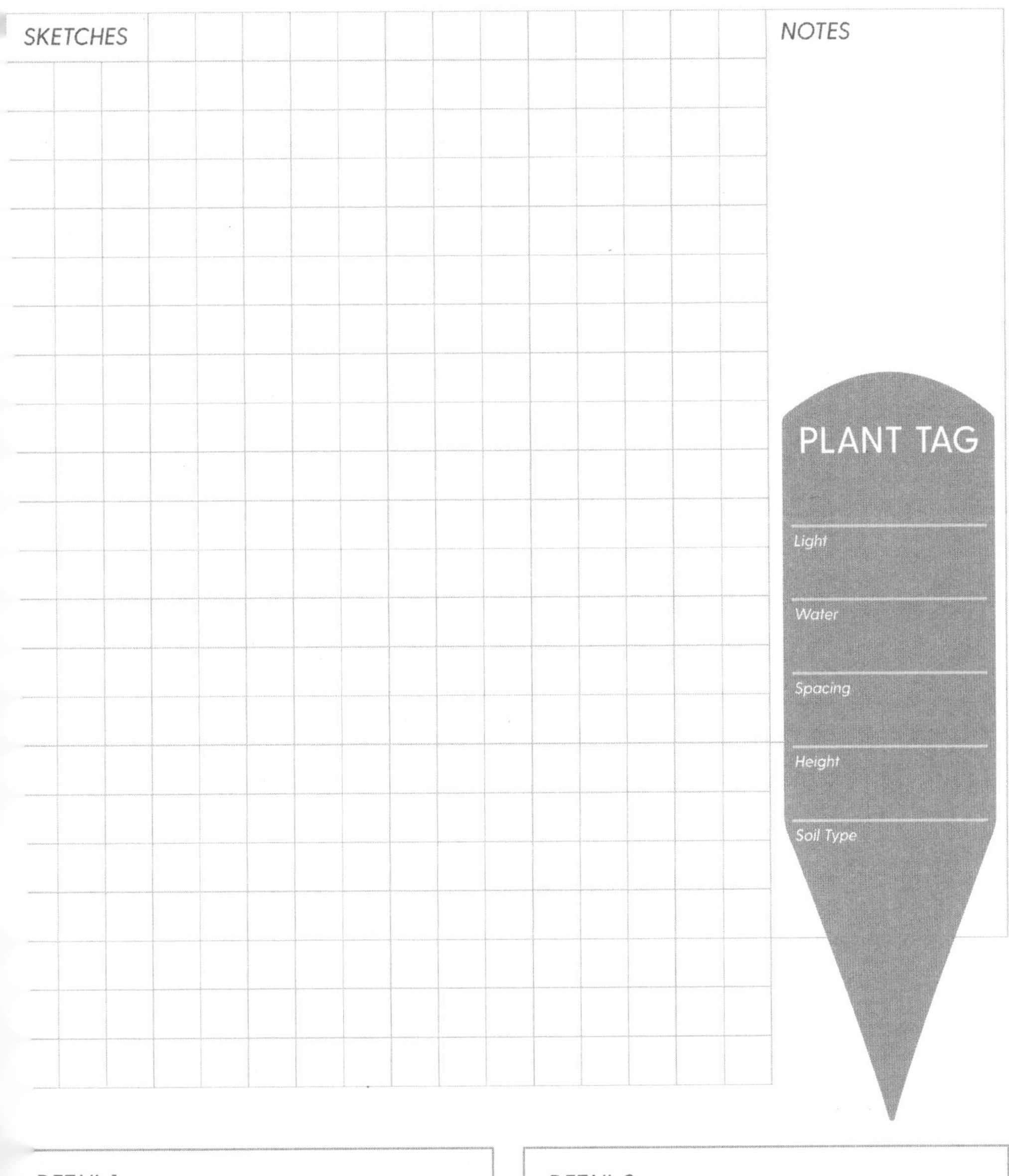

DETAIL 1

DETAIL 2

FAMILY
GENUS
SPECIES

DATE OF ENTRY

ACQUIRED FROM

SEED GROWN
Date Sown

PURCHASED
Supplier & Location

CUTTING

FIELD COLLECTED
Date & Location:
Did you do this sh*t ethically?

SOIL RECIPE

FERTILIZER REGIMEN

Amount of Water

Amount of Light

NOTES

Known Pests

Natural Habitat

Best Cultivation Environment

Why/How I haplessly MURDERED this plant:

SEASONAL OBSERVATIONS

Year One

SPRING	SUMMER	AUTUMN	WINTER

Year Two

SPRING	SUMMER	AUTUMN	WINTER

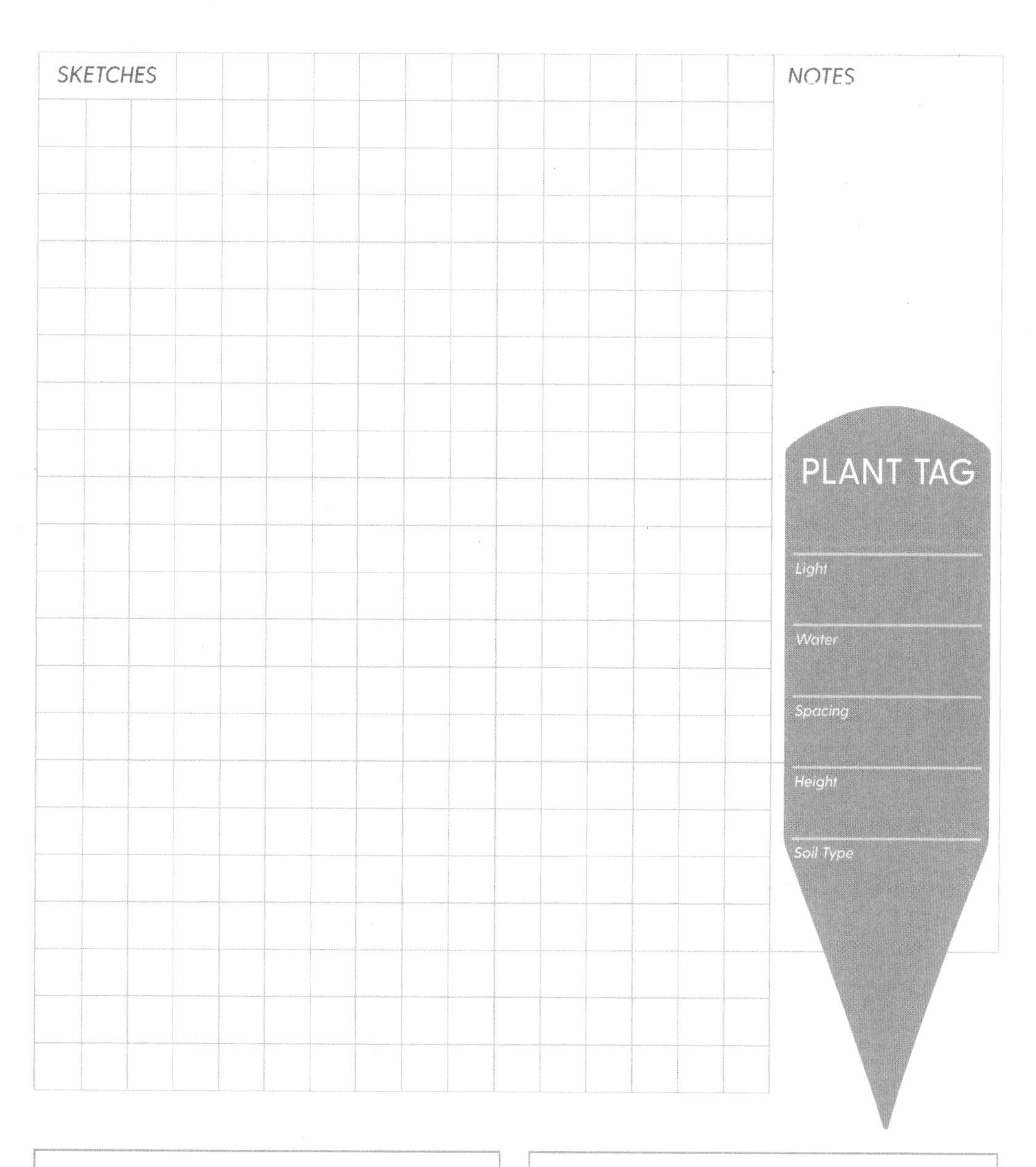

DETAIL 1

DETAIL 2

FAMILY

GENUS

SPECIES

DATE OF ENTRY

ACQUIRED FROM

SEED GROWN	PURCHASED	CUTTING	FIELD COLLECTED
Date Sown	Supplier & Location		Date & Location: Did you do this sh*t ethically?

SOIL RECIPE

FERTILIZER REGIMEN

Amount of Water

Amount of Light

NOTES

Known Pests

Natural Habitat

Best Cultivation Environment

Why/How I haplessly MURDERED this plant:

SEASONAL OBSERVATIONS

Year One

SPRING	SUMMER	AUTUMN	WINTER

Year Two

SPRING	SUMMER	AUTUMN	WINTER

SKETCHES

NOTES

PLANT TAG

Light

Water

Spacing

Height

Soil Type

DETAIL 1

DETAIL 2

FAMILY

GENUS

SPECIES

DATE OF ENTRY

ACQUIRED FROM

SEED GROWN

Date Sown

PURCHASED

Supplier & Location

CUTTING

FIELD COLLECTED

Date & Location:

Did you do this sh*t ethically?

SOIL RECIPE

FERTILIZER REGIMEN

Amount of Water

Amount of Light

NOTES

Known Pests

Natural Habitat

Best Cultivation Environment

Why/How I haplessly MURDERED this plant:

SEASONAL OBSERVATIONS

Year One

SPRING

SUMMER

AUTUMN

WINTER

Year Two

SPRING

SUMMER

AUTUMN

WINTER

SKETCHES

NOTES

PLANT TAG

Light

Water

Spacing

Height

Soil Type

DETAIL 1

DETAIL 2

FAMILY

GENUS

SPECIES

DATE OF ENTRY

ACQUIRED FROM

SEED GROWN	PURCHASED	CUTTING	FIELD COLLECTED
Date Sown	Supplier & Location		Date & Location: Did you do this sh*t ethically?

SOIL RECIPE

FERTILIZER REGIMEN

Amount of Water

Amount of Light

NOTES

Known Pests

Natural Habitat

Best Cultivation Environment

Why/How I haplessly MURDERED this plant:

SEASONAL OBSERVATIONS

Year One	SPRING	SUMMER	AUTUMN	WINTER
Year Two	SPRING	SUMMER	AUTUMN	WINTER

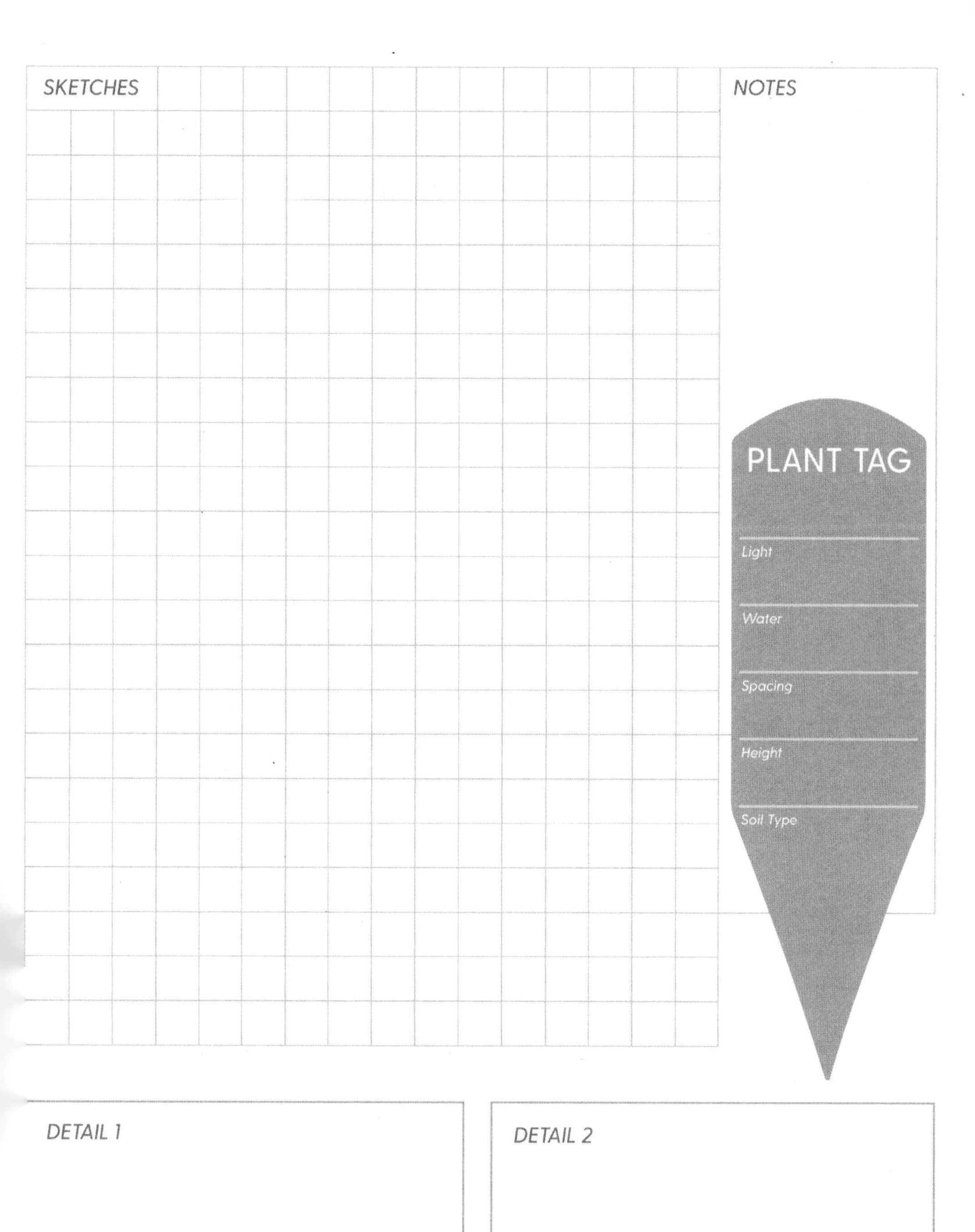

DETAIL 1

DETAIL 2

FAMILY

GENUS

SPECIES

DATE OF ENTRY

ACQUIRED FROM

SEED GROWN	PURCHASED	CUTTING	FIELD COLLECTED
Date Sown	Supplier & Location		Date & Location: Did you do this sh*t ethically?

SOIL RECIPE

FERTILIZER REGIMEN

Amount of Water

Amount of Light

NOTES

Known Pests

Natural Habitat

Best Cultivation Environment

Why/How I haplessly MURDERED this plant:

SEASONAL OBSERVATIONS

	SPRING	SUMMER	AUTUMN	WINTER
Year One				
Year Two				

SKETCHES

NOTES

PLANT TAG

Light

Water

Spacing

Height

Soil Type

DETAIL 1

DETAIL 2

FAMILY

GENUS

SPECIES

DATE OF ENTRY

ACQUIRED FROM

SEED GROWN	PURCHASED	CUTTING	FIELD COLLECTED
Date Sown	Supplier & Location		Date & Location: Did you do this sh*t ethically?

SOIL RECIPE

FERTILIZER REGIMEN

Amount of Water

Amount of Light

NOTES

Known Pests

Natural Habitat

Best Cultivation Environment

Why/How I haplessly MURDERED this plant:

SEASONAL OBSERVATIONS

Year One

SPRING	SUMMER	AUTUMN	WINTER

Year Two

SPRING	SUMMER	AUTUMN	WINTER

SKETCHES

NOTES

PLANT TAG

Light

Water

Spacing

Height

Soil Type

DETAIL 1

DETAIL 2

FAMILY

GENUS

SPECIES

DATE OF ENTRY

ACQUIRED FROM

SEED GROWN	PURCHASED	CUTTING	FIELD COLLECTED
Date Sown	Supplier & Location		Date & Location: Did you do this sh*t ethically?

SOIL RECIPE

FERTILIZER REGIMEN

Amount of Water

Amount of Light

NOTES

Known Pests

Natural Habitat

Best Cultivation Environment

Why/How I haplessly MURDERED this plant:

SEASONAL OBSERVATIONS

Year One

SPRING	SUMMER	AUTUMN	WINTER

Year Two

SPRING	SUMMER	AUTUMN	WINTER

SKETCHES

NOTES

PLANT TAG

Light

Water

Spacing

Height

Soil Type

DETAIL 1

DETAIL 2

FAMILY

GENUS

SPECIES

DATE OF ENTRY

ACQUIRED FROM

SEED GROWN	PURCHASED	CUTTING	FIELD COLLECTED
Date Sown	Supplier & Location		Date & Location:
			Did you do this sh*t ethically?

SOIL RECIPE

FERTILIZER REGIMEN

Amount of Water

Amount of Light

NOTES

Known Pests

Natural Habitat

Best Cultivation Environment

Why/How I haplessly MURDERED this plant:

SEASONAL OBSERVATIONS

Year One	SPRING	SUMMER	AUTUMN	WINTER
Year Two	SPRING	SUMMER	AUTUMN	WINTER

SKETCHES

NOTES

PLANT TAG

Light

Water

Spacing

Height

Soil Type

DETAIL 1

DETAIL 2

FAMILY

GENUS

SPECIES

DATE OF ENTRY

ACQUIRED FROM

SEED GROWN	PURCHASED	CUTTING	FIELD COLLECTED
Date Sown	Supplier & Location		Date & Location: Did you do this sh*t ethically?

SOIL RECIPE

FERTILIZER REGIMEN

Amount of Water

Amount of Light

NOTES

Known Pests

Natural Habitat

Best Cultivation Environment

Why/How I haplessly MURDERED this plant:

SEASONAL OBSERVATIONS

Year One

SPRING	SUMMER	AUTUMN	WINTER

Year Two

SPRING	SUMMER	AUTUMN	WINTER

SKETCHES

NOTES

PLANT TAG

Light

Water

Spacing

Height

Soil Type

DETAIL 1

DETAIL 2

FAMILY

GENUS

SPECIES

DATE OF ENTRY

ACQUIRED FROM

SEED GROWN	PURCHASED	CUTTING	FIELD COLLECTED
Date Sown	Supplier & Location		Date & Location: Did you do this sh*t ethically?

SOIL RECIPE

FERTILIZER REGIMEN

Amount of Water

Amount of Light

NOTES

Known Pests

Natural Habitat

Best Cultivation Environment

Why/How I haplessly MURDERED this plant:

SEASONAL OBSERVATIONS

	SPRING	SUMMER	AUTUMN	WINTER
Year One				
Year Two				

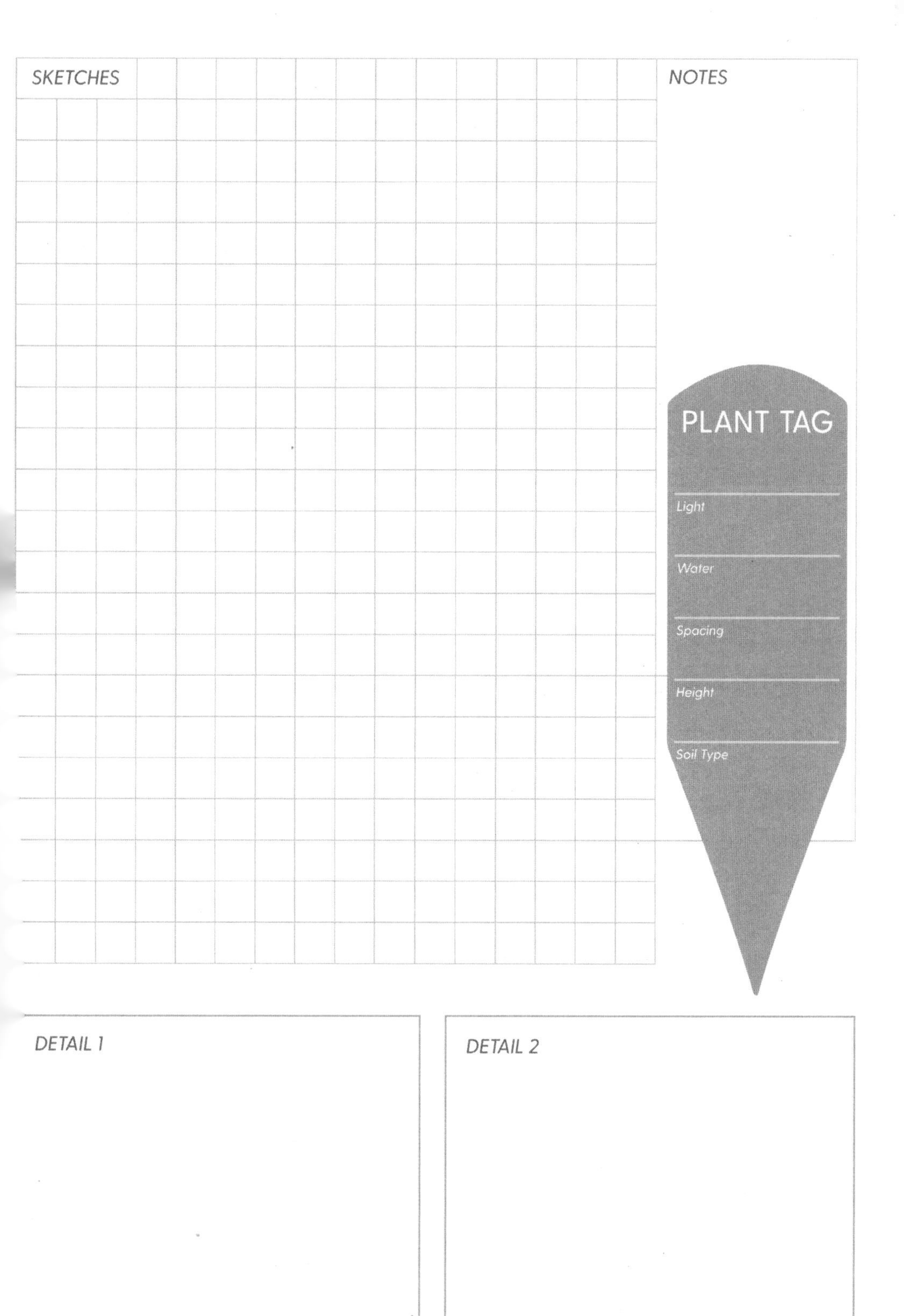
SKETCHES
NOTES
PLANT TAG
Light
Water
Spacing
Height
Soil Type
DETAIL 1
DETAIL 2

FAMILY

GENUS

SPECIES

DATE OF ENTRY

ACQUIRED FROM

SEED GROWN
Date Sown

PURCHASED
Supplier & Location

CUTTING

FIELD COLLECTED
Date & Location:
Did you do this sh*t ethically?

SOIL RECIPE

FERTILIZER REGIMEN

Amount of Water

Amount of Light

NOTES

Known Pests

Natural Habitat

Best Cultivation Environment

Why/How I haplessly MURDERED this plant:

SEASONAL OBSERVATIONS

Year One

SPRING

SUMMER

AUTUMN

WINTER

Year Two

SPRING

SUMMER

AUTUMN

WINTER

SKETCHES

NOTES

PLANT TAG

Light

Water

Spacing

Height

Soil Type

DETAIL 1

DETAIL 2

FAMILY

GENUS

SPECIES

DATE OF ENTRY

ACQUIRED FROM

SEED GROWN	PURCHASED	CUTTING	FIELD COLLECTED
Date Sown	Supplier & Location		Date & Location: Did you do this sh*t ethically?

SOIL RECIPE

FERTILIZER REGIMEN

Amount of Water

Amount of Light

NOTES

Known Pests

Natural Habitat

Best Cultivation Environment

Why/How I haplessly MURDERED this plant:

SEASONAL OBSERVATIONS

Year One

SPRING	SUMMER	AUTUMN	WINTER

Year Two

SPRING	SUMMER	AUTUMN	WINTER

SKETCHES

NOTES

PLANT TAG

Light

Water

Spacing

Height

Soil Type

DETAIL 1

DETAIL 2

FAMILY

GENUS

SPECIES

DATE OF ENTRY

ACQUIRED FROM

SEED GROWN

Date Sown

PURCHASED

Supplier & Location

CUTTING

FIELD COLLECTED

Date & Location:

Did you do this sh*t ethically?

SOIL RECIPE

FERTILIZER REGIMEN

Amount of Water

Amount of Light

NOTES

Known Pests

Natural Habitat

Best Cultivation Environment

Why/How I haplessly MURDERED this plant:

SEASONAL OBSERVATIONS

Year One

SPRING	SUMMER	AUTUMN	WINTER

Year Two

SPRING	SUMMER	AUTUMN	WINTER

SKETCHES

NOTES

PLANT TAG

Light

Water

Spacing

Height

Soil Type

DETAIL 1

DETAIL 2

FAMILY	
GENUS	
SPECIES	

DATE OF ENTRY

ACQUIRED FROM

SEED GROWN	PURCHASED	CUTTING	FIELD COLLECTED
Date Sown	Supplier & Location		Date & Location: Did you do this sh*t ethically?

SOIL RECIPE

FERTILIZER REGIMEN

Amount of Water

Amount of Light

NOTES

Known Pests

Natural Habitat

Best Cultivation Environment

Why/How I haplessly MURDERED this plant:

SEASONAL OBSERVATIONS

	SPRING	SUMMER	AUTUMN	WINTER
Year One				
Year Two				

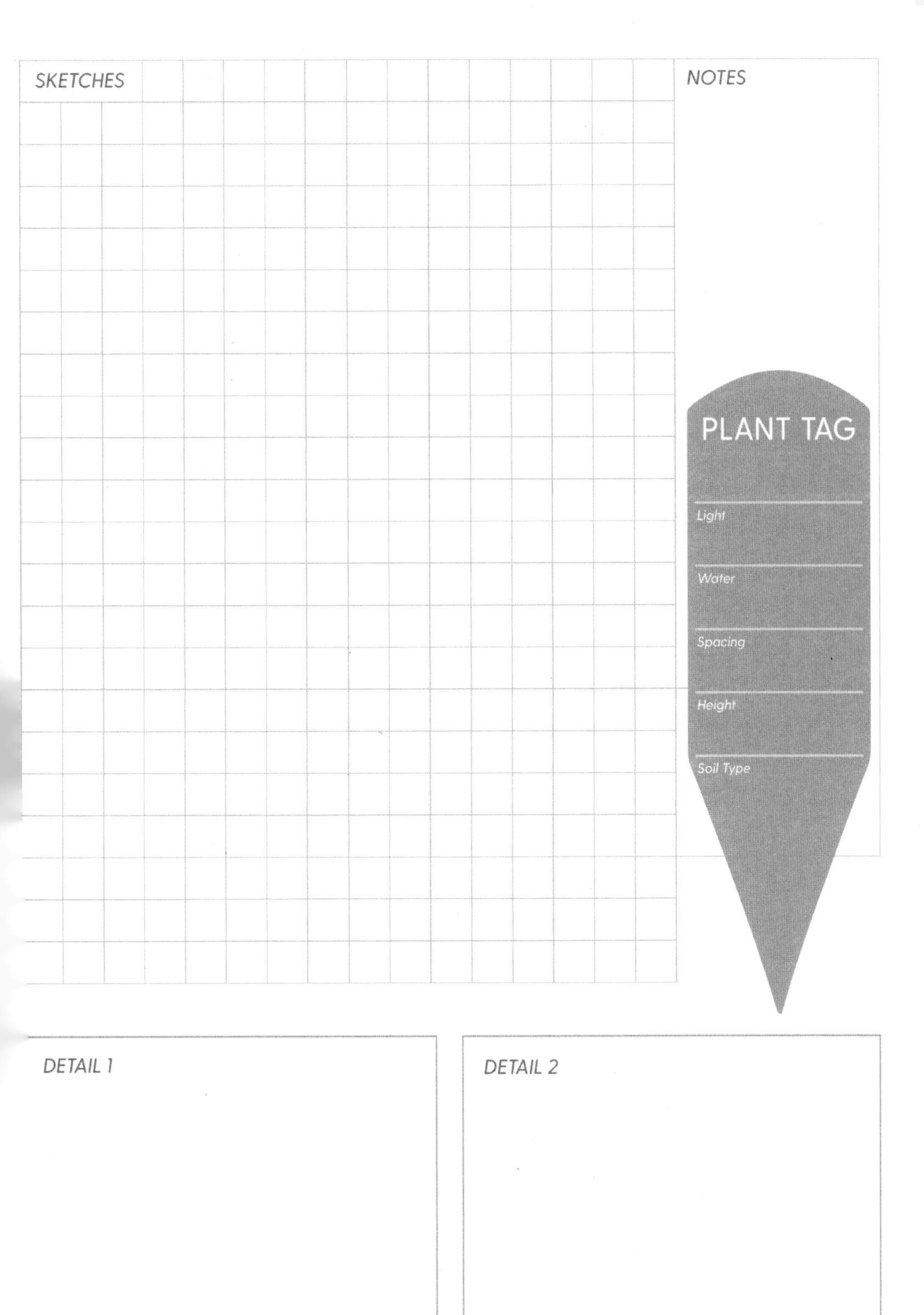

DETAIL 1

DETAIL 2

FAMILY

GENUS

SPECIES

DATE OF ENTRY

ACQUIRED FROM

SEED GROWN	PURCHASED	CUTTING	FIELD COLLECTED
Date Sown	Supplier & Location		Date & Location: Did you do this sh*t ethically?

SOIL RECIPE

FERTILIZER REGIMEN

Amount of Water

Amount of Light

NOTES

Known Pests

Natural Habitat

Best Cultivation Environment

Why/How I haplessly MURDERED this plant:

SEASONAL OBSERVATIONS

Year One	SPRING	SUMMER	AUTUMN	WINTER
Year Two	SPRING	SUMMER	AUTUMN	WINTER

SKETCHES

NOTES

PLANT TAG

Light

Water

Spacing

Height

Soil Type

DETAIL 1

DETAIL 2

FAMILY	
GENUS	
SPECIES	

DATE OF ENTRY

ACQUIRED FROM

SEED GROWN	PURCHASED	CUTTING	FIELD COLLECTED
Date Sown	Supplier & Location		Date & Location: Did you do this sh*t ethically?

SOIL RECIPE

FERTILIZER REGIMEN

Amount of Water

Amount of Light

NOTES

Known Pests

Natural Habitat

Best Cultivation Environment

Why/How I haplessly MURDERED this plant:

SEASONAL OBSERVATIONS

	SPRING	SUMMER	AUTUMN	WINTER
Year One				
Year Two				

SKETCHES

NOTES

PLANT TAG

Light

Water

Spacing

Height

Soil Type

DETAIL 1

DETAIL 2

FAMILY

GENUS

SPECIES

DATE OF ENTRY

ACQUIRED FROM

SEED GROWN	PURCHASED	CUTTING	FIELD COLLECTED
Date Sown	Supplier & Location		Date & Location: Did you do this sh*t ethically?

SOIL RECIPE

FERTILIZER REGIMEN

Amount of Water

Amount of Light

NOTES

Known Pests

Natural Habitat

Best Cultivation Environment

Why/How I haplessly MURDERED this plant:

SEASONAL OBSERVATIONS

Year One

SPRING	SUMMER	AUTUMN	WINTER

Year Two

SPRING	SUMMER	AUTUMN	WINTER

SKETCHES

NOTES

PLANT TAG

Light

Water

Spacing

Height

Soil Type

DETAIL 1

DETAIL 2

FAMILY

GENUS

SPECIES

DATE OF ENTRY

ACQUIRED FROM

SEED GROWN	PURCHASED	CUTTING	FIELD COLLECTED
Date Sown	Supplier & Location		Date & Location: Did you do this sh*t ethically?

SOIL RECIPE

FERTILIZER REGIMEN

Amount of Water

Amount of Light

NOTES

Known Pests

Natural Habitat

Best Cultivation Environment

Why/How I haplessly MURDERED this plant:

SEASONAL OBSERVATIONS

Year One	SPRING	SUMMER	AUTUMN	WINTER
Year Two	SPRING	SUMMER	AUTUMN	WINTER

SKETCHES

NOTES

PLANT TAG

Light

Water

Spacing

Height

Soil Type

DETAIL 1

DETAIL 2

FAMILY

GENUS

SPECIES

DATE OF ENTRY

ACQUIRED FROM

SEED GROWN	PURCHASED	CUTTING	FIELD COLLECTED
Date Sown	Supplier & Location		Date & Location: Did you do this sh*t ethically?

SOIL RECIPE

FERTILIZER REGIMEN

Amount of Water

Amount of Light

NOTES

Known Pests

Natural Habitat

Best Cultivation Environment

Why/How I haplessly MURDERED this plant:

SEASONAL OBSERVATIONS

Year One

SPRING	SUMMER	AUTUMN	WINTER

Year Two

SPRING	SUMMER	AUTUMN	WINTER

SKETCHES

NOTES

PLANT TAG

Light

Water

Spacing

Height

Soil Type

DETAIL 1

DETAIL 2

FAMILY

GENUS

SPECIES

DATE OF ENTRY

ACQUIRED FROM

SEED GROWN	PURCHASED	CUTTING	FIELD COLLECTED
Date Sown	Supplier & Location		Date & Location: Did you do this sh*t ethically?

SOIL RECIPE

FERTILIZER REGIMEN

Amount of Water

Amount of Light

NOTES

Known Pests

Natural Habitat

Best Cultivation Environment

Why/How I haplessly MURDERED this plant:

SEASONAL OBSERVATIONS

Year One	SPRING	SUMMER	AUTUMN	WINTER
Year Two	SPRING	SUMMER	AUTUMN	WINTER

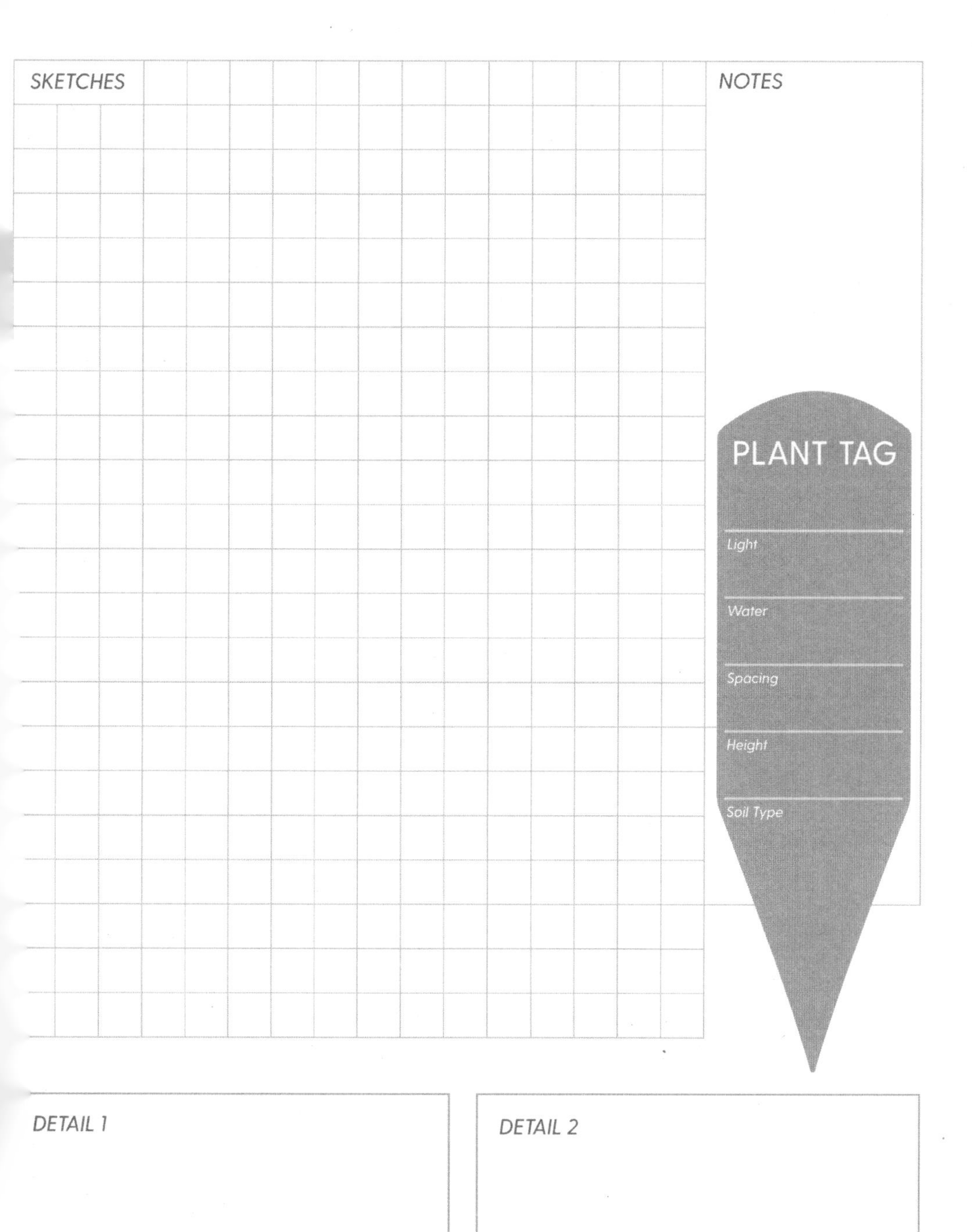

DETAIL 1

DETAIL 2

FAMILY

GENUS

SPECIES

DATE OF ENTRY

ACQUIRED FROM

SEED GROWN	PURCHASED	CUTTING	FIELD COLLECTED
Date Sown	Supplier & Location		Date & Location: Did you do this sh*t ethically?

SOIL RECIPE

FERTILIZER REGIMEN

Amount of Water

Amount of Light

NOTES

Known Pests

Natural Habitat

Best Cultivation Environment

Why/How I haplessly MURDERED this plant:

SEASONAL OBSERVATIONS

Year One

SPRING	SUMMER	AUTUMN	WINTER

Year Two

SPRING	SUMMER	AUTUMN	WINTER

SKETCHES
NOTES
PLANT TAG
Light
Water
Spacing
Height
Soil Type
DETAIL 1
DETAIL 2

FAMILY

GENUS

SPECIES

DATE OF ENTRY

ACQUIRED FROM

SEED GROWN	PURCHASED	CUTTING	FIELD COLLECTED
Date Sown	Supplier & Location		Date & Location: Did you do this sh*t ethically?

SOIL RECIPE

FERTILIZER REGIMEN

Amount of Water

Amount of Light

NOTES

Known Pests

Natural Habitat

Best Cultivation Environment

Why/How I haplessly MURDERED this plant:

SEASONAL OBSERVATIONS

Year One

SPRING	SUMMER	AUTUMN	WINTER

Year Two

SPRING	SUMMER	AUTUMN	WINTER

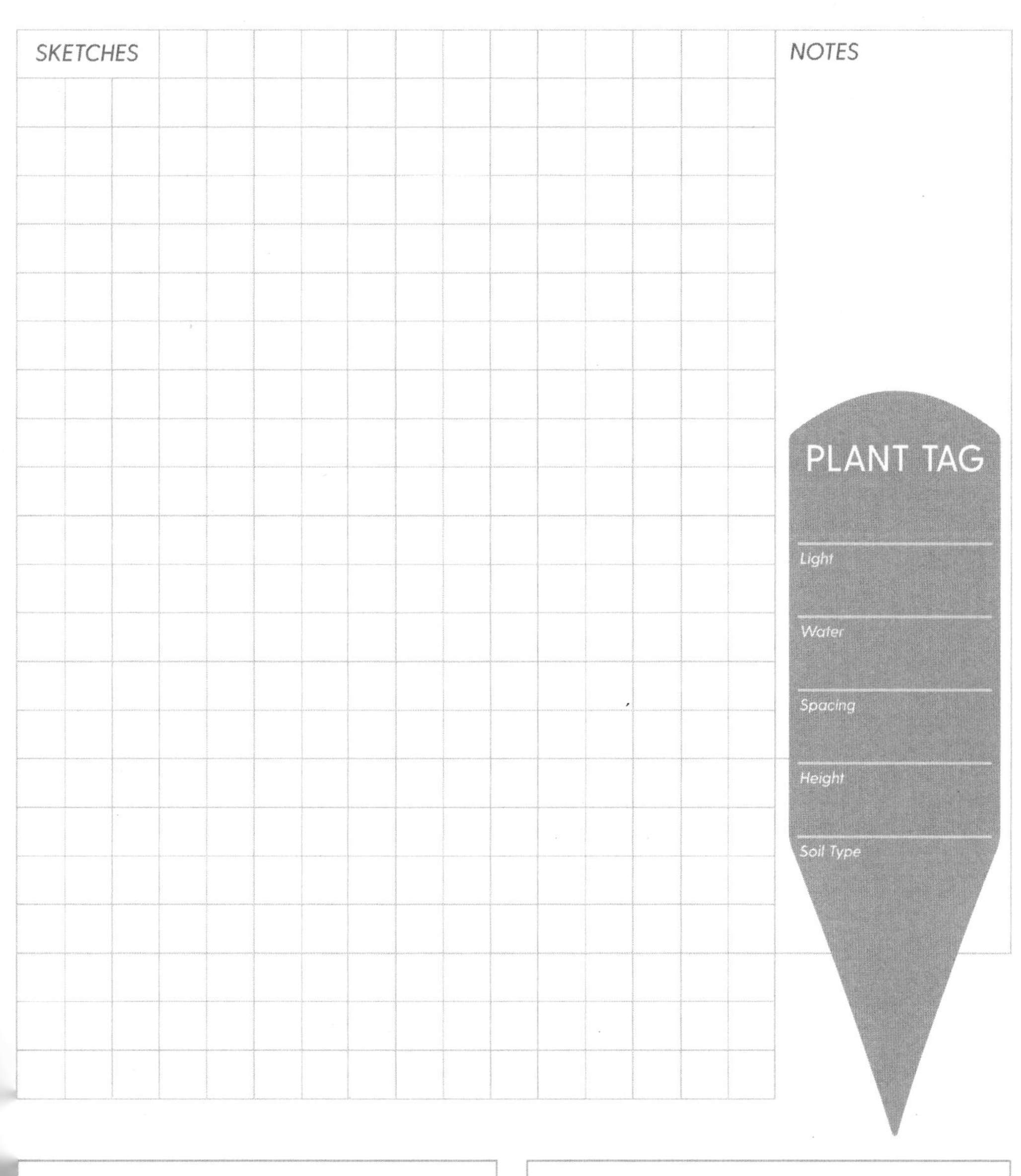

DETAIL 1

DETAIL 2

FAMILY

GENUS

SPECIES

DATE OF ENTRY

ACQUIRED FROM

SEED GROWN	PURCHASED	CUTTING	FIELD COLLECTED
Date Sown	Supplier & Location		Date & Location: Did you do this sh*t ethically?

SOIL RECIPE

FERTILIZER REGIMEN

Amount of Water

Amount of Light

NOTES

Known Pests

Natural Habitat

Best Cultivation Environment

Why/How I haplessly MURDERED this plant:

SEASONAL OBSERVATIONS

Year One

SPRING	SUMMER	AUTUMN	WINTER

Year Two

SPRING	SUMMER	AUTUMN	WINTER

SKETCHES

NOTES

PLANT TAG

Light

Water

Spacing

Height

Soil Type

DETAIL 1

DETAIL 2

FAMILY

GENUS

SPECIES

DATE OF ENTRY

ACQUIRED FROM

SEED GROWN	PURCHASED	CUTTING	FIELD COLLECTED
Date Sown	Supplier & Location		Date & Location: Did you do this sh*t ethically?

SOIL RECIPE

FERTILIZER REGIMEN

Amount of Water

Amount of Light

NOTES

Known Pests

Natural Habitat

Best Cultivation Environment

Why/How I haplessly MURDERED this plant:

SEASONAL OBSERVATIONS

Year One

SPRING	SUMMER	AUTUMN	WINTER

Year Two

SPRING	SUMMER	AUTUMN	WINTER

SKETCHES

NOTES

PLANT TAG

Light

Water

Spacing

Height

Soil Type

DETAIL 1

DETAIL 2

FAMILY

GENUS

SPECIES

DATE OF ENTRY

ACQUIRED FROM

SEED GROWN	PURCHASED	CUTTING	FIELD COLLECTED
Date Sown	Supplier & Location		Date & Location: Did you do this sh*t ethically?

SOIL RECIPE

FERTILIZER REGIMEN

Amount of Water

Amount of Light

NOTES

Known Pests

Natural Habitat

Best Cultivation Environment

Why/How I haplessly MURDERED this plant:

SEASONAL OBSERVATIONS

Year One

SPRING	SUMMER	AUTUMN	WINTER

Year Two

SPRING	SUMMER	AUTUMN	WINTER

SKETCHES

NOTES

PLANT TAG

Light

Water

Spacing

Height

Soil Type

DETAIL 1

DETAIL 2

FAMILY

GENUS

SPECIES

DATE OF ENTRY

ACQUIRED FROM

SEED GROWN	PURCHASED	CUTTING	FIELD COLLECTED
Date Sown	Supplier & Location		Date & Location: Did you do this sh*t ethically?

SOIL RECIPE

FERTILIZER REGIMEN

Amount of Water

Amount of Light

NOTES

Known Pests

Natural Habitat

Best Cultivation Environment

Why/How I haplessly MURDERED this plant:

SEASONAL OBSERVATIONS

Year One

SPRING	SUMMER	AUTUMN	WINTER

Year Two

SPRING	SUMMER	AUTUMN	WINTER

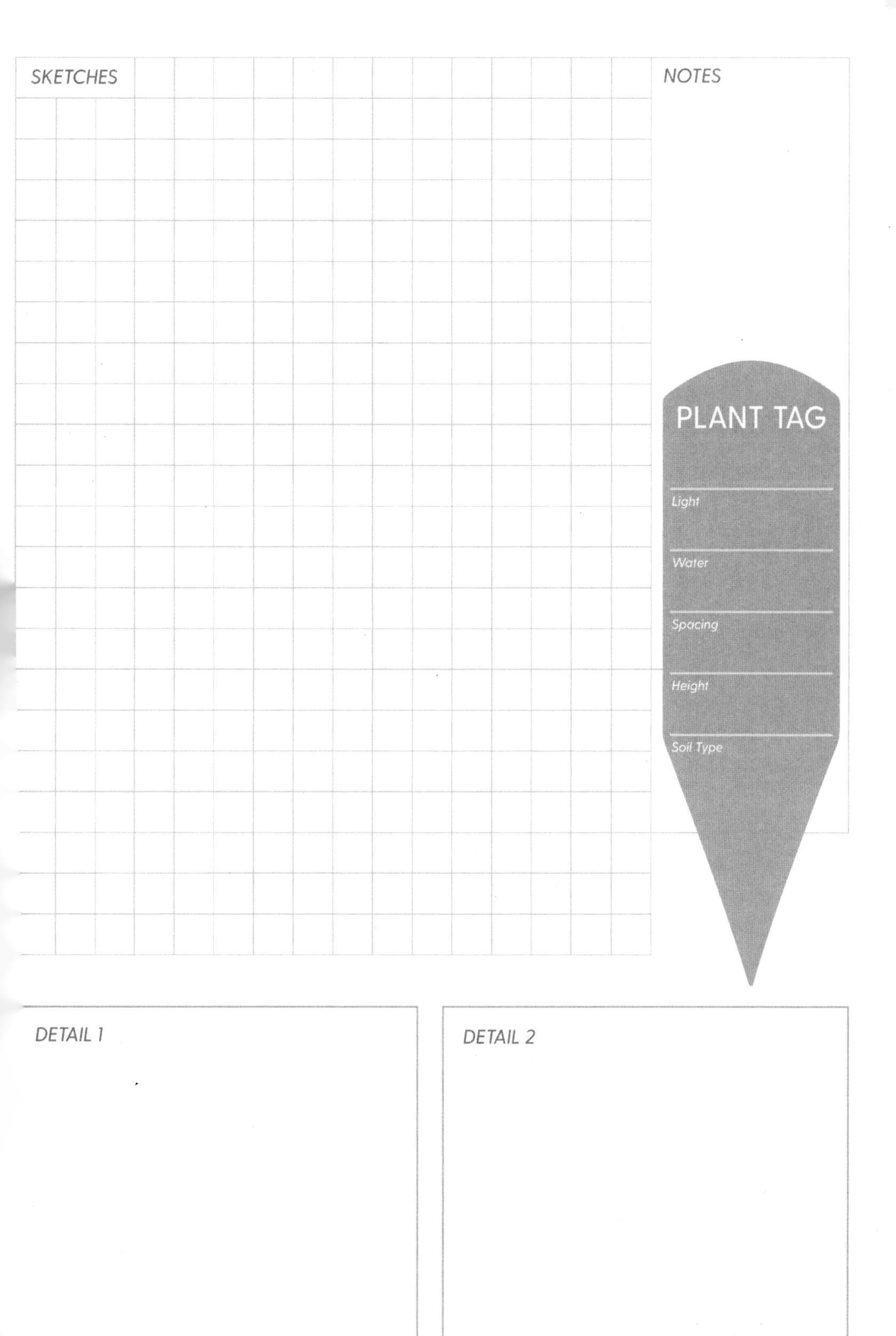
SKETCHES
NOTES
PLANT TAG
Light
Water
Spacing
Height
Soil Type
DETAIL 1
DETAIL 2

FAMILY

GENUS

SPECIES

DATE OF ENTRY

ACQUIRED FROM

SEED GROWN	PURCHASED	CUTTING	FIELD COLLECTED
Date Sown	Supplier & Location		Date & Location: Did you do this sh*t ethically?

SOIL RECIPE

FERTILIZER REGIMEN

Amount of Water

Amount of Light

NOTES

Known Pests

Natural Habitat

Best Cultivation Environment

Why/How I haplessly MURDERED this plant:

SEASONAL OBSERVATIONS

Year One

SPRING	SUMMER	AUTUMN	WINTER

Year Two

SPRING	SUMMER	AUTUMN	WINTER

SKETCHES

NOTES

PLANT TAG

Light

Water

Spacing

Height

Soil Type

DETAIL 1

DETAIL 2

FAMILY

GENUS

SPECIES

DATE OF ENTRY

ACQUIRED FROM

SEED GROWN	PURCHASED	CUTTING	FIELD COLLECTED
Date Sown	Supplier & Location		Date & Location: Did you do this sh*t ethically?

SOIL RECIPE

FERTILIZER REGIMEN

Amount of Water

Amount of Light

NOTES

Known Pests

Natural Habitat

Best Cultivation Environment

Why/How I haplessly MURDERED this plant:

SEASONAL OBSERVATIONS

Year One

SPRING	SUMMER	AUTUMN	WINTER

Year Two

SPRING	SUMMER	AUTUMN	WINTER

SKETCHES

NOTES

PLANT TAG

Light

Water

Spacing

Height

Soil Type

DETAIL 1

DETAIL 2

FAMILY

GENUS

SPECIES

DATE OF ENTRY

ACQUIRED FROM

SEED GROWN	PURCHASED	CUTTING	FIELD COLLECTED
Date Sown	*Supplier & Location*		*Date & Location:* *Did you do this sh*t ethically?*

SOIL RECIPE

FERTILIZER REGIMEN

Amount of Water

Amount of Light

NOTES

Known Pests

Natural Habitat

Best Cultivation Environment

Why/How I haplessly MURDERED this plant:

SEASONAL OBSERVATIONS

Year One	SPRING	SUMMER	AUTUMN	WINTER
Year Two	SPRING	SUMMER	AUTUMN	WINTER

SKETCHES

NOTES

PLANT TAG

Light

Water

Spacing

Height

Soil Type

DETAIL 1

DETAIL 2

FAMILY

GENUS

SPECIES

DATE OF ENTRY

ACQUIRED FROM

SEED GROWN	PURCHASED	CUTTING	FIELD COLLECTED
Date Sown	Supplier & Location		Date & Location: Did you do this sh*t ethically?

SOIL RECIPE

FERTILIZER REGIMEN

Amount of Water

Amount of Light

NOTES

Known Pests

Natural Habitat

Best Cultivation Environment

Why/How I haplessly MURDERED this plant:

SEASONAL OBSERVATIONS

	SPRING	SUMMER	AUTUMN	WINTER
Year One				
Year Two				

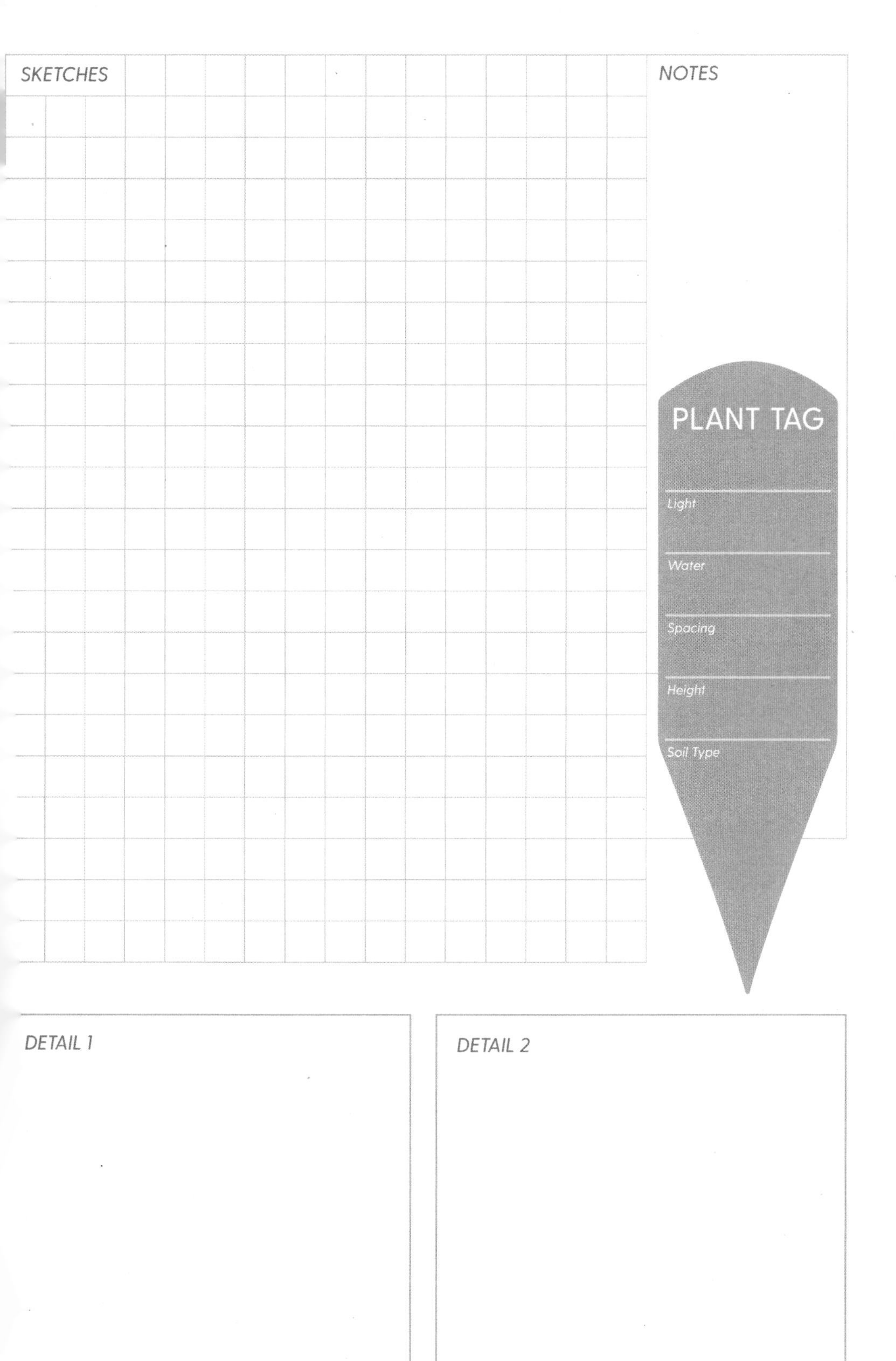

DETAIL 1

DETAIL 2

FAMILY

GENUS

SPECIES

DATE OF ENTRY

ACQUIRED FROM

SEED GROWN	PURCHASED	CUTTING	FIELD COLLECTED
Date Sown	Supplier & Location		Date & Location: Did you do this sh*t ethically?

SOIL RECIPE

FERTILIZER REGIMEN

Amount of Water

Amount of Light

NOTES

Known Pests

Natural Habitat

Best Cultivation Environment

Why/How I haplessly MURDERED this plant:

SEASONAL OBSERVATIONS

	SPRING	SUMMER	AUTUMN	WINTER
Year One				
Year Two				

SKETCHES

NOTES

PLANT TAG

Light

Water

Spacing

Height

Soil Type

DETAIL 1

DETAIL 2

FAMILY	
GENUS	
SPECIES	

DATE OF ENTRY

ACQUIRED FROM

SEED GROWN	PURCHASED	CUTTING	FIELD COLLECTED
Date Sown	Supplier & Location		Date & Location: Did you do this sh*t ethically?

SOIL RECIPE

FERTILIZER REGIMEN

Amount of Water

Amount of Light

NOTES

Known Pests

Natural Habitat

Best Cultivation Environment

Why/How I haplessly MURDERED this plant:

SEASONAL OBSERVATIONS

Year One	SPRING	SUMMER	AUTUMN	WINTER
Year Two	SPRING	SUMMER	AUTUMN	WINTER

SKETCHES

NOTES

PLANT TAG

Light

Water

Spacing

Height

Soil Type

DETAIL 1

DETAIL 2

FAMILY

GENUS

SPECIES

DATE OF ENTRY

ACQUIRED FROM

SEED GROWN	PURCHASED	CUTTING	FIELD COLLECTED
Date Sown	Supplier & Location		Date & Location: Did you do this sh*t ethically?

SOIL RECIPE

FERTILIZER REGIMEN

Amount of Water

Amount of Light

NOTES

Known Pests

Natural Habitat

Best Cultivation Environment

Why/How I haplessly MURDERED this plant:

SEASONAL OBSERVATIONS

Year One

SPRING	SUMMER	AUTUMN	WINTER

Year Two

SPRING	SUMMER	AUTUMN	WINTER

SKETCHES

NOTES

PLANT TAG

Light

Water

Spacing

Height

Soil Type

DETAIL 1

DETAIL 2

FAMILY

GENUS

SPECIES

DATE OF ENTRY

ACQUIRED FROM

SEED GROWN	PURCHASED	CUTTING	FIELD COLLECTED
Date Sown	Supplier & Location		Date & Location:
			Did you do this sh*t ethically?

SOIL RECIPE

FERTILIZER REGIMEN

Amount of Water

Amount of Light

NOTES

Known Pests

Natural Habitat

Best Cultivation Environment

Why/How I haplessly MURDERED this plant:

SEASONAL OBSERVATIONS

Year One

SPRING	SUMMER	AUTUMN	WINTER

Year Two

SPRING	SUMMER	AUTUMN	WINTER

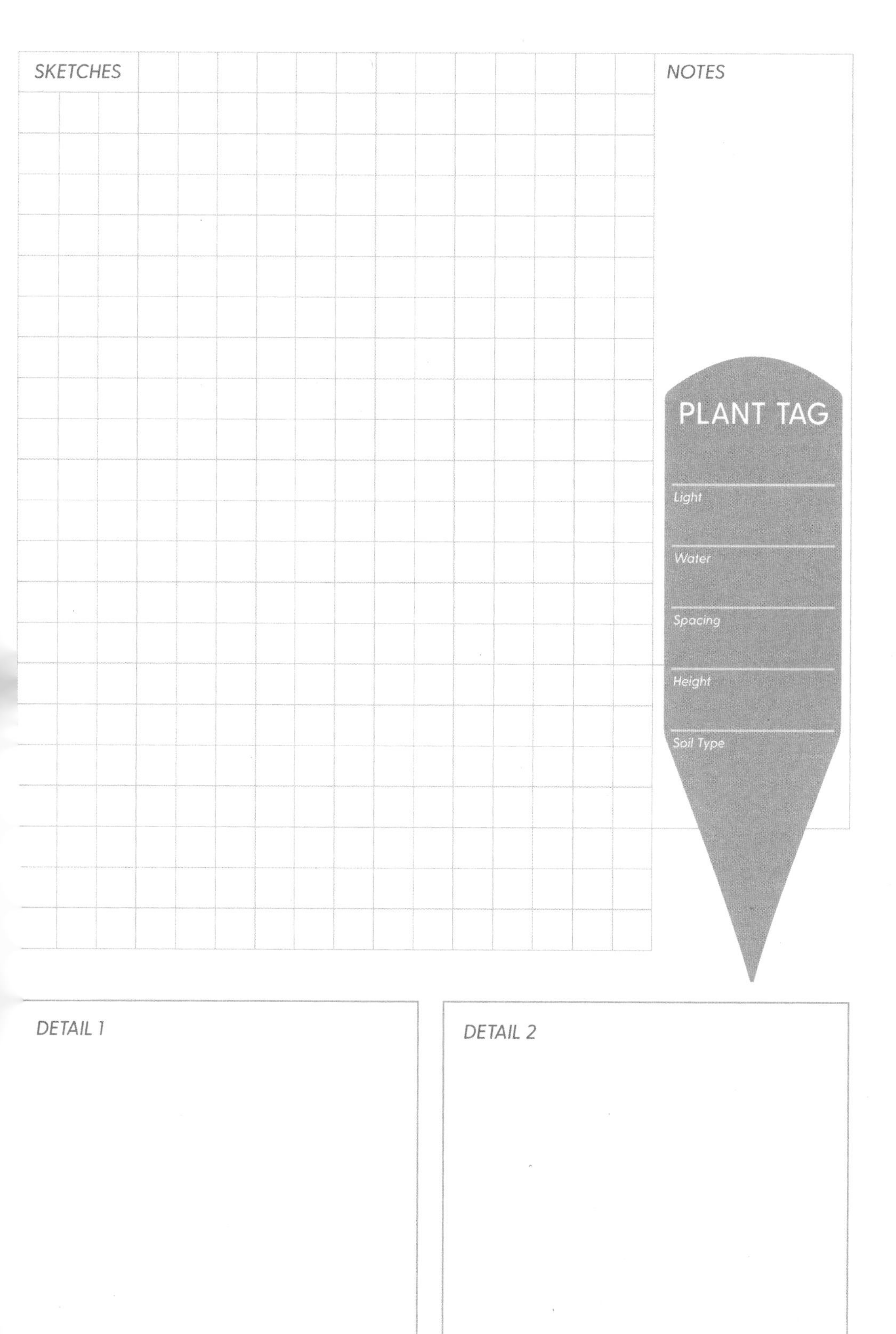

DETAIL 1

DETAIL 2

FAMILY

GENUS

SPECIES

DATE OF ENTRY

ACQUIRED FROM

SEED GROWN	PURCHASED	CUTTING	FIELD COLLECTED
Date Sown	Supplier & Location		Date & Location: Did you do this sh*t ethically?

SOIL RECIPE

FERTILIZER REGIMEN

Amount of Water

Amount of Light

NOTES

Known Pests

Natural Habitat

Best Cultivation Environment

Why/How I haplessly MURDERED this plant:

SEASONAL OBSERVATIONS

Year One	SPRING	SUMMER	AUTUMN	WINTER
Year Two	SPRING	SUMMER	AUTUMN	WINTER

SKETCHES

NOTES

PLANT TAG

Light

Water

Spacing

Height

Soil Type

DETAIL 1

DETAIL 2

FAMILY

GENUS

SPECIES

DATE OF ENTRY

ACQUIRED FROM

SEED GROWN	PURCHASED	CUTTING	FIELD COLLECTED
Date Sown	Supplier & Location		Date & Location: Did you do this sh*t ethically?

SOIL RECIPE

FERTILIZER REGIMEN

Amount of Water

Amount of Light

NOTES

Known Pests

Natural Habitat

Best Cultivation Environment

Why/How I haplessly MURDERED this plant:

SEASONAL OBSERVATIONS

Year One

SPRING	SUMMER	AUTUMN	WINTER

Year Two

SPRING	SUMMER	AUTUMN	WINTER

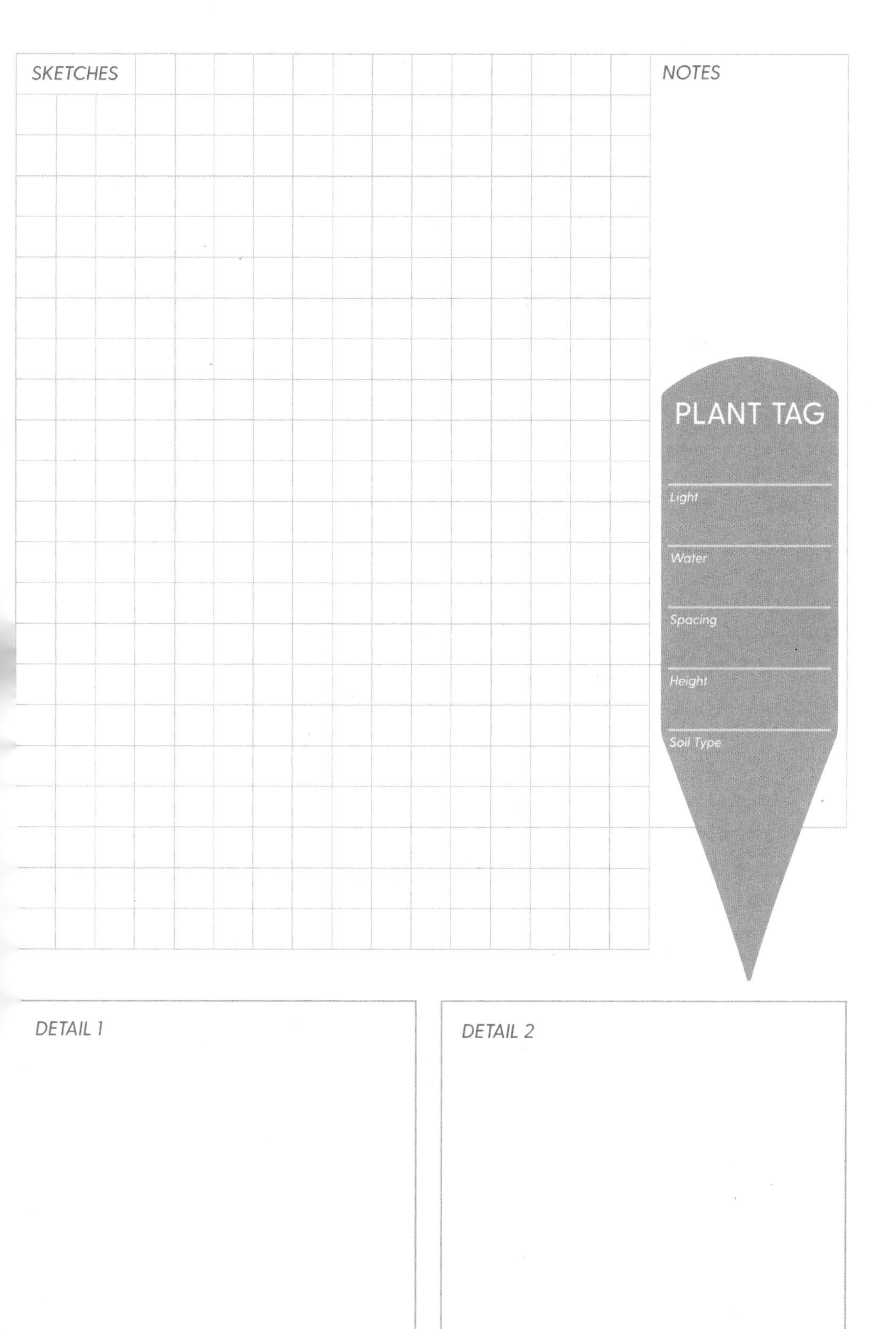
SKETCHES
NOTES
PLANT TAG
Light
Water
Spacing
Height
Soil Type
DETAIL 1
DETAIL 2

SOME DAMN SOIL RECIPES

Name: *Date:*

Name: *Date:*

Name: *Date:*

MORE RECIPES

Call It Something:	*Date:*

Hello My Name Is:	*Date:*

Whisper This, and It Shall Come:	*Date:*

SOME DAMN SOIL RECIPES

Name:	*Date:*

Name:	*Date:*

Name:	*Date:*

MORE RECIPES

Call It Something:	*Date:*

Hello My Name Is:	*Date:*

Whisper This, and It Shall Come:	*Date:*

SOME DAMN SOIL RECIPES

Name:	*Date:*

Name:	*Date:*

Name:	*Date:*

MORE RECIPES

Call It Something:	*Date:*

Hello My Name Is:	*Date:*

Whisper This, and It Shall Come:	*Date:*

SOME DAMN SOIL RECIPES

Name:	*Date:*

Name:	*Date:*

Name:	*Date:*

MORE RECIPES

Call It Something:	*Date:*

Hello My Name Is:	*Date:*

Whisper This, and It Shall Come:	*Date:*

GROW *a* DAMN

GROW *a* DAMN